Jean C.
Vermes

Enjoying Life as a Sportsman's Wife

Stackpole Books
Harrisburg, Pa.

Library of Congress catalog card number: 65-13387

Published by The Stackpole Company
Cameron and Kelker Streets
Harrisburg, Pa. 17105

Manufactured in the U.S.A.
by The Telegraph Press
010 Harrisburg, Pa.

Contents

4

Enjoying Life as a Sportsman's Wife

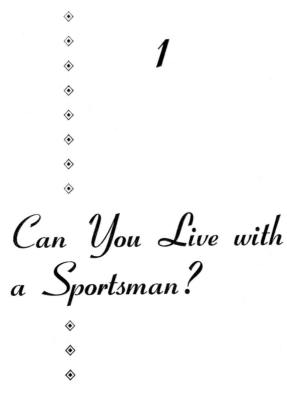

1

Can You Live with a Sportsman?

Can you live with a sportsman? You can, but it isn't always easy. The wife of the angler may wonder about this as she's wakened some morning in spring, long before dawn, by the toot of an automobile horn. It will be Dad's fishing pals, waiting for him to join them; and there he'll be, all dressed and ready to go, at an hour when she ordinarily couldn't rouse him with three alarm clocks and a Chinese gong.

Although fishing is a year-round sport, it is usually in spring that the urge to get out into natural surroundings overcomes the fisherman. The hunter will be more likely to get restless in the fall, when the first leaves begin turning. Then you can expect him to start cleaning his guns and gear, checking over his supplies, and casting out broad hints that he needs to get away from the treadmill. He will spend hours pouring over the hunting pages of his favorite magazines and newspapers to get up-to-date information on the current season.

In these fifty states, there are eighteen million fishermen and thirteen million hunters. If your husband is one of these millions, you have probably pondered the question of why you should have to put up with this seasonal migration, when there is plenty of food in the deep freeze at home and enough fresh air and greenery out in your own back yard or the neighboring park. Look at it this way: You're never going to know exactly why, so you might as well just relax and enjoy life as a sportman's wife.

One summer William K. Carpenter, president of the International Game Fish Association, caught and released twenty-three tuna in a week of fishing in Newfoundland. He kept the twenty-fourth for good luck, because it was his five-hundredth in a lifetime. What Mrs. Carpenter thought about all this was not reported. There are women who knit twenty-three sweaters in a row and then unravel them again, for the mere sensation of handling the wool and clicking the needles. So we must be charitable and take the attitude that if, to a man, fishing in itself is a pleasure, then let him have his fun.

When hunting woodchuck, a sportsman who is a pistol enthusiast will spend two hours stalking a chuck and drawing up on him inch by inch, only to see him finally disappear in alarm. The hunter could easily have hit him at distances up to four hundred yards with a good rifle, but he prefers the challenge of the more difficult sport. Another man will test his skill and endurance by chasing a clapper rail across the marsh, through mud and water, beset by swarms of mosquitoes. When the bird finally takes flight and is shot down, he is good for nothing but the taxidermist's shop—for, as Oscar Godbout of the *New York Times* says about the rail's edibility, "Give one to a man unfed for a few weeks and he will eat one."

No matter how much he may protest, your husband does not hunt or fish for any known practical reason. It goes much deeper than that. The outdoorsman is moved by the desires and ambitions which have motivated his sex ever since the cave man hunted and fished back in the stone age. Deep down inside his heart, modern man still harbors the basic instincts of his distant forebears. Any explanation of his devotion to his hobby that has any connection with modern life is pure rationalization.

SOME WIFELY RESPONSES

There is no use trying to find out why he really wants to hunt and fish in this era of the supermarket. The main thing to do is try to appreciate the physical, mental, and emotional benefits he receives from his hobby. After that, your aim should be to try to fit it in with your activities, so that it can become a constructive part of your life together. This does not necessarily mean that you should become a sportswoman yourself (although there are many women who do). It means that you should plan an equally pleasant occupation for yourself on the occasions when he is away, so that he comes home to a happy reception and is glad to be back. It means that you should find an attractive outdoor hobby of your own that will lead to greater rapport between you. It means that you should learn something about his sports activities, so that you can discuss them with him sympathetically, even when you don't enter into them actively.

You might begin, for example, by complimenting him on having chosen so inexpensive a hobby. According to government statistics, a fisherman spends on the average only $106.26 a year for the purpose, and a hunter just $79.34, even including his average proportionate contribution of thirty-one cents to the duck stamp program—which is about what his wife would pay for an Easter outfit. And he derives as much pleasure from his pastime as you do from your new clothes. A mutual understanding of the basic needs which these diverse interests fulfill can lead to more harmony in the home.

When you haven't enjoyed the pleasures of the hunt, you may feel that it is unfair to be expected to gut and pick birds or scale and clean fish. And it is. However, messy handling can be avoided by turning over venison and other game to a butcher for cleaning and hanging, cutting, and wrapping for the freezer. Fish, after being cleaned by the fisherman, can go into the freezer, too. This way you will have available, any time you expect guests for dinner, a different and exceptionally good meal that they will be bound to remember. Fish is easy to cook, and venison is no more difficult than beef or mutton. Wild birds are simply roasted faster and at higher temperatures than domestic fowl. There is no good reason why you cannot acquire a reputation for gourmet cookery as your share of your husband's hobby.

Add game and fish cookbooks to your library. There are not very many, and because they are not common you won't have too much competition if you want to go in for exotic-sounding recipes like Pheasant a la Bohemienne, Wild Duck Greco, or Venison en Papillote. Incidentally, The London *Sunday Times* has a cooking page called "Cooking with Robert Carrier" that often features recipes for fish and game; and many American newspapers carry cooking columns by men. The latter frequently give recipes for nothing more rare than poached eggs or chicken soup, but you'll occasionally find something that suits your needs as a sportsman's wife.

While you're at it, try a few fiction or non-fiction books with animal and outdoors backgrounds. For example, *Rascal*, by Sterling North, available in a paperback edition (Avon, 1963), tells a charming story of a boy and his pet raccoon, and at the same time has many detailed accounts of his fishing expeditions in the Wisconsin rivers and lakes. Both you and your fisherman husband would enjoy reading this one. And you may get a kick out of *Eagle in the Bathtub*, by Jule Mannix (Ballantine, 1964), telling of her adventures with a husband who kept, among other things, a pet eagle. Your husband could get enjoyment out of Daniel P. Mannix' *All Things Both Great and Small*, (McGraw-Hill, 1963), in which Jule's husband tells of his adventures hunting with the eagle in lieu of a falcon.

Look over the various sports magazines, like *Outdoor Life, Field and Stream*, and *Sports Afield*. They often contain articles by and about sportswomen, or the wives of sportsmen. Magazines like *National Geographic* often have sports articles as well as travel pieces. Publications like *True* Magazine contain murder mystery stories along with adventure and sports material, and *Esquire* Magazine can give your husband the story of a hunting trip while providing you with inside dope on the lives of Elizabeth Taylor and Sue Lyon. *National Wildlife* Magazine is slanted to the nature lover and conservationist, as well as the hunter and fisherman.

Why not subscribe to one of these publications for both of you? You can read about travel, mystery, movie stars, or natural history; and he can learn more about his favorite outdoor sport. If you should happen to find that your interests have begun to overlap, and you are giving the hunting and fishing pieces more than a passing glance, while he is becoming intrigued by articles about Indian Cliff Dwellers, ax murderesses, actresses, and Monarch butterflies, so much the better.

WHAT THE MEN GET OUT OF IT

There are all kinds of sportsmen, just as there are all kinds of men with any hobby or profession. One kind is the gadgeteer, who follows every fad and keeps the salesmen in the sports departments of the big stores happy. The gadgeteer may in time develop into one of those overloaded outdoorsmen who carry along so much clothing and equipment they come home all tired out just from hauling and portaging. Then there is the absent-minded fellow who keeps his gear down to a sensible minimum, but in so doing usually forgets some vital item. Of course there is the early bird, who can't wait for the season to start, whether it is for deer, duck, or trout. Long before it is time to go forth with gun or rod, this fellow is polishing up his gear or tying flies or practicing down at the target range. Comes the season (after a long, dry spell) and—you guessed it—the governor declares the woods out of bounds for fishing and hunting to prevent forest fires. If you haven't recognized your own particular sportsman yet, perhaps he is the last-minute one, who on the eve of his trip into the great outdoors can't find half his equipment; or the accident-prone one who always comes home swathed in Band Aids. There are extrovert husbands who broadcast their experiences to one and all, and introverts who keep them a close secret. As in business or social life, there are the conformists who go along with what the other fellows are doing, and the individualists who prefer to go out for iguanas or piranhas when the rest of the gang are happy with rabbits and red snappers.

If what goes into his outdoor hobby varies from man to man, so does what he gets out of it—although all sportsmen have some things in common. The hunter and fisherman both get a certain amount of exercise as a result of their hobbies, and in this pushbutton era that is a great advantage to both man and wife. A man who exercises improves his circulation, which in turn helps the heart that keeps him in good physical condition. Good circulation also stimulates the brain and helps keep it in normal working order. The better your husband's physical health, the longer you'll have him with you; and the more active his brain, the better job he can do of providing for his family. If you can persuade him to supplement this outdoor exercise, which he does not always get on a regular basis, you will be doing a favor to him and yourself. The sportsman derives the benefits, also, of more unpolluted air and undiluted sunshine than his brother who takes all his exercise indoors in the gym, bowling alley, or billiard parlor. The beauty of the wide outdoor panoramas is psychologically uplifting as well, and getting back to nature makes a man feel like a Daniel Boone or Davy Crocket, if only for a few hours. There is also the feeling of being at one with nature, which the late Herbert Hoover expressed in his book *Fishing For Fun* (Random House, 1963):

"In our outdoor life we get repose from the troubles of soul that this vast complex of civilization imposes upon us in our working hours and restless nights."

WHAT YOU GET OUT OF IT

While you certainly can benefit indirectly from your husband's strength of body, liveliness of mind, and peace of soul, which he acquires in his trips to the outdoors, you may be wondering whether any direct benefits are possible for you. There are many. The six or seven days a year your sportsman spends engaging in his hobby can be a welcome vacation period for you, during which you are free to indulge yourself, improve yourself, or engage in independent recreation. You can, if you choose, sleep late, dress like a frump, eat gooey feminine snacks, and serve the family meals out of a can. What a relief from the stringent discipline of the other fifty-one weeks in the year! Should you prefer, you can go in the opposite direction: exercising, going on a strict diet, buying a new style in clothes, getting a going-over at the beauty

salon, or improving your mind with some sort of constructive hobby. Just don't be too self-righteous about
it when your husband comes home. Let him appreciate
the results, while you pretend it was not contrived but
just happened naturally.

Another antidote for boredom is to plan some form of
recreation when Daddy is away, either by yourself, with
friends, or with the children. You can get tickets to a
play, the ballet, or a concert—choosing something that you
know your husband doesn't care about, so that you probably wouldn't have gone together anyway. You'll be
sparing him an ordeal and giving yourself a boost. Or
take the kids on a picnic, to a ball game, or to a museum.
There are plenty of interesting things to do; so there
is no point spending a day, a week end, or a week just
puttering around feeling vaguely sorry for yourself, like
Penelope in Homer's Odyssey, waiting for your hero
to come home.

IT MAY INTEREST YOU TO LEARN . . .

When your sportsman does return with a bag of game
or a creel of fish, would it surprise you to know that his
expeditions do the countryside more good than harm?
You may possibly have felt that his invasions of field,
wood, and stream were purely selfish indulgence. This is
far from true. The taxes that he pays through his hunting
licenses, fishing permits, and equipment, go to the states
and territories of the United States for the improvement
of sport fishing and hunting. The American Fishing Tackle
Manufacturers Association, the Sporting Arms and
Ammunition Manufacturers' Institute, and the sportsmen

themselves, want to pay these taxes on tackle, firearms, and cartridges to aid in wildlife restoration programs. The preservation of wildlife which provides game for the hunter also provides for the preservation of natural wilderness areas, such as the Bob Marshall Wilderness in Montana, the Teton Wilderness Area in Wyoming, the John Muir Wilderness Area in California, and other sections of the new nine-and-a-tenth-million-acre National Wilderness Preservation System.

William E. Towell, Director, Missouri Conservation Commission, has this to say about the contributions to their country of the hunter and fisherman (*National Wildlife,* October-November, 1964):

"Sportsmen-conservationists are a powerful force in this country, and not only in matters concerned with hunting and fishing opportunities. They spearheaded the national water pollution control movement, outdoor recreation legislation, control of pesticides, soil and water management legislation, public lands protection, and many other important conservation campaigns. Take away hunting and fishing as incentives, and the hunter and fisherman as financial backers, and the wildlife conservation movement in this country would die."

A LITTLE SPORTSMAN TALK

If you read Sterling North's *Rascal*, as recommended, you may enjoy the human-interest story of a boy and his pet. But you also may think to yourself, during the fishing episodes, "What is all this talk of lures and leaders, and dry flies and wet flies, and streamers and fly reels?" If your husband is a fisherman, you should learn a little of what fishing is about: the differences between fly fishing, bait casting, spin casting, bottom fishing, and trolling, and the sport to be derived from these various methods. There is a kind of fishing appropriate to any husband's tastes and personality, from big game fishing for the energetic and muscular to jug fishing for the man who just wants to relax in a boat while waiting for the fish to jump.

There is even greater variety in hunting than in fishing. The hunter can go after big game, medium game, and small game. He can hunt shore birds, marsh birds, and upland birds. Each hunter has his favorite branch of the sport, and his wife can understand a little of its appeal if she learns something of how it is done and the satisfactions it brings.

Do you ever have trouble understanding what your sportsman husband is talking about when he returns from a trip with the boys? Do you know the meaning of "backlash," other than its political implications? Is a "grunion" to you some new kind of onion? Or did you know that it is a fish that comes ashore to spawn once a year in the middle of the night, and is caught by Californians in their nightshirts with their bare hands? Do you realize what a "mad moon" means to a grouse hunter? Do you think a "pointer" is something used by an old-fashioned schoolteacher to direct her pupils' attention to the blackboard? A little study of the hunting and fishing glossaries (chapters 10 and 11) in this book will familiarize you with some of the common terms. When, in spite of this, your sportsman uses an unfamiliar word, try to remember it so that you can look it up in the dictionary and surprise him some time by knowing its meaning. If he frustrates you by never using the word again, get even by bringing it up in casual conversation. Inquire nonchalantly, "Been doing any popping lately?" or "Got any new leaks in your sneak box?" You'll wow him!

Some women go beyond learning the language of sports and attempt to learn the sports themselves. This is great if the husband is agreeable and the woman's interest sincere. Hunting and fishing are not fads to be taken up one year and dropped the next, like parlor games. Both husband and wife must really want her to engage in the sport. If this situation does not exist, then it is better for her to forget it and take up some other outdoor hobby like bird-watching, nature photography, skin diving, or skiing.

Then when your sportsman returns from refreshing his soul in wood, field, or stream, you can listen to the tall tales of his fishing and hunting adventures (though you've heard similar ones scores of times before) secure in the knowledge that you will be able to counter later with whoppers of your own. Should he exaggerate—as sportsmen are occasionally inclined to do—conceal your smile. He'll love you for it; and you'll love him for the man of nature that he is.

2

What Really Makes the Sportsman Tick?

What makes the sportsman tick? Twenty-five thousand years ago, when his ancestors were scratching pictures of game on the walls of caves, wives didn't need to ask themselves that question. They knew the answer. Grown tired of a diet of fruit and nuts and having discovered the use of fire in cooking, he went out to hunt and fish to satisfy a basic instinct, hunger. The discovery of the spear and the bow, the net, rod, and line, helped considerably in this effort.

Hunting and fishing became even more sophisticated

with the invention of the gun and the artificial lure. By now domesticated animals were the most important source of food, and hunting and fishing had become sports rather than a way of life. While at one time every man hunted to provide food for his family, today—when it is no longer a necessity—a third of the adult male population still hunts and fishes. What impels them to do so? What is it that makes these men different from the bowlers, the golfers, the gardeners, the do-it-yourselfers?

They can be as varied in background as George Washington, Theodore Roosevelt, and Ernest Hemingway; as Herbert Hoover and Izaak Walton. George Washington, the aristocrat, went fox hunting. Roosevelt and Hemingway, the extroverted outdoorsmen, hunted big game. The late Herbert Hoover, a quiet, introverted man, enjoyed the tranquility of fishing a peaceful stream or lake, as did that other famous fisherman Izaak Walton.

Your own sportsman's choices will be a reflection of his character and environment. If he is a big game hunter he will be one sort of man. Small game hunting will appeal to someone else again. Sometimes the differences in quarry indicate principally a difference in locale. If you are inland dwellers he will go for upland game birds, while if you dwell along the shore, the shore birds will be his object. If you live near the watering places around the country, then waterfowl will be his logical goal. Your income can also determine your sportsman's interests. The man who goes to Nova Scotia for salmon or to Bimini for marlin may indeed be more enterprising than one who catches trout in a local brook, or one who surf casts along the adjacent shore. In many cases, however, he may just have more time and money to spend.

SPECIAL IDIOSYNCRASY GROUPS

All outdoorsmen have some common denominators. Although they don't have to fish and hunt for game to keep their families from starvation, they are still unconsciously impelled to act as the providers and protectors of their families. This, you must admit, is a good thing. Having these basic instincts, a sportsman is generally a good family man. He makes a good pal for his male offspring, and a strong masculine figure for his daughters to idealize. But good family man, pal, and idol that he may be, there are still certain personal idiosyncrasies that distinguish him from his fellows. You may recognize yours among the following:

The Gadgeteer Fisherman. He takes a new gadget along on each fishing trip, anything from a transparent plug case for his belt to a transistorized fish call. The weight of the plug case restricts his circulation, and the fish call lures only minnows. But does he give up? No indeed. Next trip will find him taking along an electronic fishing thermometer or a vest-pocket line-drier. Don't discourage him. There's no telling what fascinating adventures he will encounter because of them. Wander through the sports section of your department store occasionally when you are out shopping. If you should happen on some such gadget, pick one up for him as a surprise. He'll be touched.

The Overloaded Hunter. He is only traveling fifty miles for a week end in the familiar state game area, but he takes along a map and compass, an extra hunting coat, a raincoat, and enough camping equipment for a three-week African safari. He will wear too many clothes, get overheated and damp from perspiration, and come home with a bad cold, blaming it all on the weather. Nurse him patiently through the cold, then hope that next time a few gentle hints will keep him in check. They probably won't, but you can try.

The Absent-Minded Sport. This man believes in traveling light. He eliminates every bit of unessential gear, then goes through and takes out some more. He is on the right track, certainly. He makes up a list of the essentials. He checks and doublechecks. You kiss him goodbye. He drives off in an aura of self-satisfaction. An hour later he pulls up to the front door. He has forgotten to put on his wristwatch. This man's air of efficiency is deceptive, and even after years of marriage it is apt to lull you both into a false feeling of security. Don't let it. Check over his list yourself before he leaves. You, as an objective outsider, can think of ordinary things like wristwatches and keys and eyeglasses, while his mind is concentrating on guns and ammo or fishing equipment.

The Early Bird. It is Labor Day, and you are lying on the beach soaking up the sun and wishing that the summer could last a little longer. Next to you, your husband is scanning the horizon with a pair of binoculars. The legal hunting season doesn't start until, say, October 17, but he is already looking for an early brace of geese or an advance flock of duck, coot, or brant. With the daily bag so severely limited these days and the seasons split for conservation purposes, the waterfowl hunter must enjoy much of his sport in advance and in retrospect. If the birds he finally identifies in the distance as pintails are really just herring gulls, don't disillusion him. Occasionally scan the skies yourself during the month to come. You may see a flock of mallards or canvasbacks you can report to your anxious spouse. Your bookstore can supply you with an inexpensive guide to identification.

Last-Minute Larry. While Larry's wife is quietly watching mayhem on television some evening, the screams of the murder victim will be drowned out by the cries of anguish from her husband. "Where did you put my spinning rod?" he croaks. Or, "What happened to my .225 Winchester?" This is the first notice she's been given that he expects to go fishing or hunting in the morning, but she's expected to come up with an answer or join in the search.

The secret for handling a man with this type of temperament is to give him plenty of room to keep his equipment in an orderly manner, so that it is ready for his use at a moment's notice. Don't confine him to an overcrowded cellar or hall closet. If you can afford a gun cabinet or English leather rod-and-reel cases, that's fine. If not, then be sure that the outdoorsman has a closet or corner all his own, where he can construct a rack to keep his guns clean, dry, and available, and his rods, reels, flies, and tackle in orderly array. Then when you are torn away from your thriller, you can just point a finger at the exact spot and say, "There it is," and go back to finding out whodunnit.

The Accident-Prone. This sportsman goes away for the day a happy, healthy specimen, full of vigor and optimism.

23

He comes home at night limping and groaning. If there is a gully into which someone can fall, he will be that someone. If there is a snake who hates the human race, this man is the member of it who will get bit. Wasps, flies, and gnats all seek him out. He gets gouged in a tangle with his fishing tackle and skins himself with his hunting knife. Mosquitoes follow him, skunks ambush him, and ivy poisons him. His wife can only console herself with the knowledge that many more Americans are seriously injured in accidents at home than when at work or at play. See that your husband takes along a first aid kit, learns the safety rules of gun handling if he is a hunter, and water safety precautions if he is a fisherman. Then relax. He is safer out in the woods than he is in the shower.

The Extrovert. The extrovert outdoorsman is a wonderful guy. He keeps all his friends supplied with game. He also keeps them supplied with tales of his exploits. His family and friends have their lives enriched with repeated showings of his black and whites and color slides, his stills and movies. Don't discourage him. That will sour him and make you look like a spoilsport. Send his latest story, and black and white photographs of him and his catch, to the local newspaper. You couldn't get much wider publicity for him than that. With every newspaper reader in town already familiar with his adventures, he may suddenly become modest—a good sportsman ought to, once fame strikes. That will give you a chance to describe your own exploits. If there is still a clamor for the latest shots of Dad with his limit of quail or a string of bass, you can only remind yourself, "They asked for it!"

The Introvert. This man's wife would never know, from the information she gets out of him, whether her husband had spent the week hunting and fishing in rural Quebec or living it up in downtown Montreal. He could have picked up that antlered head or mounted fish in a hock shop. When she asks him how he enjoyed his trip, he says, "Okay," or "Great," and then inquires, "So what else is new?" The problem here is usually that the man knows his wife has no real interest in his hobby, and if he were to tell her about it she would nod absently and interrupt to ask what kind of pie he wanted for dessert that night. A woman who wants her husband to confide in her should invite confidences. An hour's boning up on the particular game he was pursuing while he was away would prepare her to make more specific inquiries and receive more interesting answers.

Conformist or Individualist. Personalities aside, the outdoorsman is often influenced in his behavior by what the other fellows who share his hobby are doing. If all the boys are chasing rabbits and squirrels, so will the conformist. If Joe down the block goes out for deer, so will he. If ducks are the popular quarry, he'll be busy building duck blinds. This is in marked contrast to the actions of the individualist, who will want to hunt grizzlies if everyone else is hunting raccoon, even if it means a trip to Alaska to find them.

LIKE FATHER, LIKE SON

Hunting is often a family sport, with son and grandson following in the family tradition. The best-known members of such a family are Kermit and Jonathan Roosevelt, great-grandsons of Teddy. In 1960 Kermit, Jonathan, and Kermit, Senior, sentimentally retraced the safari that Theodore Roosevelt had made fifty years before. T. R. had some adventures with dangerously thundering rhinos. So did Jonathan. T.R. bagged a leopard. So did Kermit, Junior. Kermit, Junior, bagged a leopard, and his dad didn't; so Kermit, Senior, went back three years later to duplicate his son's feat. Richard Thorne Tjader, whose father was a contemporary of Teddy Roosevelt, also made a fifty-years-later safari to duplicate his dad's exploits. Roughing it today is quite different from roughing it yesterday, though, and the changing face of Africa may soon make the hunting safari a thing of the past.

The average hunter who follows in his father's steps is more likely to resemble Ray Bressler, the retired major league baseball player. In a recent issue of *Outdoor Life* (May, 1964), he recounted his wonderful memories of hunting with his dad—and with his baseball pals from the Cincinnati Reds—for deer and an occasional bear. As Mr. Bressler puts it, "In the lives of most men, the important dates are birthdays or anniversaries. For deer hunters, the date that stands out is the opening day of deer season." Remember that when your sportsman forgets a birthday or anniversary, and try, if you can, to understand.

Ray Bressler still remembers looking longingly out of his Flemington, Pennsylvania, school window and watching enviously as his dad and uncle packed a sled with provisions for their hunting camp. When he was a little older, he was allowed to go along, walking most of the twenty-mile route, since it was too cold to sit still and ride.

Not all fathers are anxious to have young companions

along on hunting or fishing trips, and not every boy wants to follow in Dad's footsteps. Occasionally a father may prefer to be with men his own age. Perhaps the son would rather bat a ball or drive a car or just hang around with the fellows. Father-son palship in this or any kind of endeavor can't be pushed. But if it does happen to develop, it's a fine thing for both of them, providing companionship for the older man and an example in sportsmanship for the young man to follow. A youngster's sharp eyes and strong legs are an asset in helping the older one sight downed game and fetching it for him. The boy in turn can acquire a knowledge of hunting and fishing safety, etiquette, and nature lore that will be of value to him in later life. He will learn to love the outdoors and be interested in the conservation of it and its wildlife.

IN LOVE WITH THE CURLEW

The word "love" is used advisedly here. In an issue of *Field and Stream* (November, 1961), there is an article by Byron W. Dalrymple about a historical game bird, the curlew. He is a large, long-legged, brown bird with a long, curved beak. Shooting him is illegal in the United States, because our founding fathers shot his ancestors down too liberally for eating purposes, and he has become scarce. A hundred years ago, you see, shooting was still done to a great extent for practical reasons—to provide food—and only incidentally for sport. It was Mr. Dalrymple's subtitle to his article that caught my eye. Said he, "In Mexico we got a chance to hunt a bird our forefathers loved—the curlew." Later on he talks of recreating "this continent's most romantic bird-hunting history." He mentions that his heart thumped each time he spied the birds.

You will often find references in outdoor writing to the excitement and the rapid heartbeats of the hunter as he sees his quarry, or the fisherman when he feels a tug on his line. It explains much about the outdoorsman's devotion to his sport. It has all the thrills of a love affair without any of its complications. It has many other advantages too. The lover must dress immaculately. The sportsman can wear old clothes and let his beard grow. The lover must be on his best behavior. The sportsman can eat with his elbows on the table and use indecorous language. The lover must woo his loved one. The sportsman has only to sight his prey, and if he is skillful and experienced, it is surely his. Of course, there is sometimes an elusive fish or animal. Like the elusive woman, it is the most highly prized of all. That old trout who has been fooling the anglers all summer will please the man who pulls it in more than any of the other catches he has made, and he and the rest will speak of it affectionately. A Canadian goose which was netted for banding in Wisconsin was discovered to be wearing a band that had been put on it for identification eighteen years before. The bander was ecstatic over finding a bird that had been passing over heavily hunted flyways all that time without having reached the end of the road. It was a female too, which made it even more romantic!

Donald Culross Peattie expressed this feeling in men when, in his book *An Almanac for Moderns*, written back in 1935, he said:

"It is natural that women should like the birds whose

domestic affairs can be observed under the eaves; they love the sweetest singers, the brightest plumage, the species not too shy to be seen at close range. For them the waders and swimmers, the awkward of leg, the harsh of cry, the wild of soul, have seldom the same appeal. But that which flees from men, that will men have. Women of all people ought to understand this, but they do not, quite."

So there it is, the basic difference between the man's and the woman's attitude toward nature. Woman is domesticated herself and she likes the domesticated animal. Man is not at home in the domestic state. He adjusts to it, and he can be fairly content in it, but he wants an occasional escape. A flight into the wild, among untamed creatures, is especially relaxing to him for this reason. A woman with an outdoorsman for a husband is actually lucky that her man has this opportunity to release all those repressions which make him the upstanding, hard-working, well-trained family provider that he is. Without it, who knows what he might turn to? He might grow a beard and become a beatnik, or put a bundle over his shoulder and hop a freight to distant parts. Instead he will go off once or twice a year for a few days, a week end, or a week and come back refreshed and ready to be happily domesticated until the next time. Meanwhile he'll recall his past adventures, look ahead to new ones, and live some vicariously in his favorite magazines, where he can dream of hunting wild hogs in the Philippines, cougar in Nevada, tiger in India, and boar in Hawaii; and of fishing for cutthroat trout in Alaska or salmon in Great Britain.

Enjoying Life as a Sportsman's Wife

The seasons move along differently for the sportsman from the way they do for his wife. For him spring means the start of the fresh-water fishing season, summer means the time for salt-water fish, winter means ice-fishing or fishing in Florida, and fall means hunting everywhere. (There are some animals, like rabbits and fox, on which there is no closed season in certain states; but most open seasons on game like deer and bear are in the fall.) With the woman it is different. For her, spring means a flowery chapeau, summer means children home from school, fall means redecorating the living room, winter means the Thanksgiving turkey (or Canadian goose), Christmas presents, and—hopefully—a new fur coat.

There is a connection between your husband's hobby and your own fur coat that is not so far-fetched as you might imagine. All living things on this planet exist in relation to one another. Some provide food for other animals; others provide sport for men. Still others furnish fur coats for their wives. The beaver serves a double purpose. His hide makes attractive coats for women, and his dams make ponds where brook trout thrive for the pleasure of men. According to conservationists, the beaver provides deep, shady pools where young fish can be reared and fed favorably in natural surroundings, assuring fishermen of good catches in the streams they inhabit.

Women often wonder how the outdoorsman can keep on doing the same thing year in and year out, pulling in the same fish or bagging the same birds. The answer is that he never tires of it, any more than a woman tires of shopping for clothes or redecorating the house. Ernest Hemingway put it clearly:

"When you have shot one bird flying you have shot all birds flying. They are all different and they fly in different ways but the sensation is the same and the last one is as good as the first."

3

What Does He Get from Outdoor Life?

The sportsman obviously obtains recreation and relaxation from his outdoor life. He gets the companionship of men with similar interests.

He escapes for a time the pressures of business and domestic problems. His mental and spiritual health benefit from it, and so should his physical well-being.

The hunter in particular gets plenty of physical exercise from his favorite sport, since it involves so much walking. The trout fisherman and surf caster, too, use their legs considerably.

JUST PLAIN EXERCISE

In this automotive age men don't exercise their legs as much as they should. Dr. Paul Dudley White, in an address to executives, commented concerning this: "It has been said that a five-mile walk will do more good to an unhappy businessman than all the philosophy and medicine in the world, and I rather think it is true."

Just as the outdoorsman's activities psychologically provide a change of pace, an encouragement to enterprise, and a test of skill, so they physiologically put demands on his heart, lungs, and other organs that build up his strength. They can also keep his figure in trim if indulged in frequently enough, since walking briskly uses up approximately three hundred calories an hour, and even walking at a slower pace consumes two hundred calories.

Hiking through the woods or upstream increases a man's endurance and develops the muscles of his legs. A fisherman who rows his own boat gets good exercise for his legs and abdomen, as well as giving his arms a workout. Carrying and lifting his rifle or gun helps give the hunter arm and shoulder exercise. Casting develops the fisherman's wrists, and pulling in a big one with lots of fight can be good for those arm and shoulder muscles as well.

Leg exercise, besides developing the muscles, also improves the circulation and helps the heart in its work. Since you want to keep his heart in the best possible shape, this should be good news. The heart pumps the blood along to the brain; and as the large leg muscles keep the blood moving upward to the heart, so the heart can send it to the brain cells, your husband's mental fitness is being helped along with his physical fitness. Vigorous use of the

33

leg muscles also helps to keep the diaphragm working well.

After reading all this, you may be wondering, "Why doesn't my husband have a physique like Jack La Lanne?" The answer of course is that he doesn't fish or hunt seven days a week. He will keep in even better shape, and gain more benefit from his outdoor sport, if he also engages in some other sports or exercise the year round. If he does daily calisthenics or goes down to the gym for a regular game of handball with the fellows, or plays golf a couple of times a week, then he will help keep up the physical and mental benefits gained during the seasonal exercise of hunting or fishing.

If he does not, then he should be encouraged to do so. More easily said than done, say you? You could set a good example, and perhaps get rid of some unwanted lumps and bumps yourself, by doing daily exercises to the dictation of a radio or TV fitness expert. If your local television station happens to carry the program of one of those exercise girls in tight black leotards at a time when your husband is around, you should have no trouble persuading him that this is indeed great fun.

If calisthenics doesn't work, then try engaging in some family sport. Bicycling is a good one, and fast cycling uses up five hundred calories an hour while exercising the legs vigorously. Perhaps the whole family can go down to the local bowling lanes on a regular basis, using up the calories and keeping legs and arms in condition. Swimming in the summer is one of the best all-around exercises there are, but the summer swimmers often let themselves go in winter time. A table tennis or deck tennis set in the family room could correct this imbalance.

Hunting and fishing can help keep your sportsman fit. But they will do him more good if he keeps himself fit the rest of the time, so that he goes off on his fishing or hunting expedition sound of wind and limb. He will avoid a lot of aches and pains that way; he won't suffer from stiffness or shortness of breath; and he'll feel lots younger.

REAL FRESH AIR AND SUNSHINE

Two physical benefits that your outdoorsman will get from his trips to the woods that cannot be duplicated at home are the advantages of fresh air and sunshine. The smoke from power plants, industry, dwellings, buses, and automobiles makes the problem of smog a serious one in all urban and suburban neighborhoods. In northern New Jersey, Rutgers University has a collection of plant life in its laboratories burned and shriveled from the chemical pollutants in the air. In London, New York, Los Angeles, and Donora, Pennsylvania, people have died from causes directly attributable to air pollution. Your own particular locality may not have suffered any such drastic effects; but the air is never pure, no matter how clean it may appear, until you get away from factory, home, and automobile exhausts. The trees in the country areas manufacture the oxygen that people need in order to live, and —as you may remember from biology class—they absorb the carbon dioxide that we give off in respiration.

Sunshine too is filtered through a haze of pollutants anywhere that the activities of man produce the smoke which in turn is transformed into dangerous chemicals on contact with the sun and air. "Clouds, fog, and dust in the atmosphere absorb ultraviolet rays," says the United States

Department of Agriculture. "Sunlight in cities accordingly is inferior to sunlight in open country." The sunlight and fresh air in the city, town, or suburb where you live can be improved for the benefit of yourself, your children, and your husband, if pressure is brought to bear on the authorities (1) to give the existing departments of air pollution more money to spend, and (2) to create departments of air pollution where none already exist.

Laws are being passed in certain areas to require industry to protect us from their fumes and to require automobiles to have their exhaust poisons reduced. More such laws should be put into effect. All this can be speeded up if you join with your local branch of the League of Women Voters, or some such civic organization, and encourage them to prod your legislators to action. Until such action can be obtained, be happy that your husband has a hobby that is so beneficial to his health; for the better his health, the more fun he will be to live with and the longer you will have him around.

A HEALTHY APPETITE

Still another side benefit from the outdoors hobby is a nutritional one. The exercise in the fresh air and sunshine gives a man a good appetite. He probably eats the sort of hearty breakfast that he doesn't have the time or hunger for at home. His lunch and dinner will be high in protein, since he hasn't the facilities for preparing fancy desserts and other unwanted starches that creep into his usual daily diet. As for green vegetables, don't let it worry you! Arctic explorer Vilhjalmur Stefansson once set out to prove that man could thrive entirely on a diet of meat and fish. He and a friend spent a year in the frozen north, subsisting only on this protein fare, and they returned to this country healthier than when they had started out.

Here again, as with the exercise bit, it would be a fine thing if your sportsman could be persuaded to follow his outdoors régime throughout the rest of the year. Try serving him large breakfasts when he returns home from his next hunting or fishing expedition, and see whether he will eat them. He may be tempted, and it will be good for his health, since the hardest work of the day is usually done in the morning. When a person starts out with a light breakfast, he tires more easily and is inclined to eat a larger lunch than necessary—which results in a drowsy afternoon and an entire day that is not so efficient or healthful as it should be. Why not cut down on sweets with all meals, making bigger breakfasts and smaller desserts the new rule? It will be good for everyone's health, may trim down a couple of waistlines, and might cut down on the children's dentist bills as well.

A SENSE OF ROMANTIC INDIVIDUALISM

In addition to adding variety, activity, and the development of specialized skills to his life, outdoor sports give a man other psychological lifts. This is the age of the organization man and the team worker, the chain store and the amalgamation of companies. From childhood on, a man is taught adjustment to "the group." This is all very well, but it represses a basic human desire for individualism. Out in the wilds a man is on his own. He is doing what he wants because he wants to do it, and the rest of the world be damned!

37

Out in the country—although the nearest town may be just beyond the bend of the river, or over the hill—he can pretend it isn't there, and can identify with the frontiersman of Early-American days or with the lord of the manor of a few hundred years ago. These men didn't have to make themselves part of the company team. They *were* the team. They didn't have to study human relations on the job. Anybody who couldn't relate to them knew what he could do.

The only actual relic of the lord-of-the-manor days that we have in this country is Robert David Lion Gardiner, the owner of Gardiner's Island, which has been in his family since 1639. These 3,300 rolling acres of wilderness, beaches, and fields located off the end of Long Island abound in duck, pheasant, wild turkey, and deer; and the Gardiners hold hunting parties in the fall, just as their ancestors did in an earlier time.

Much of the rest of the sporting population of the United States hunts and fishes in public hunting and fishing areas rather than on private preserves. Massachusetts alone has eighteen of these areas. In a sense, of course, every American citizen owns his own little piece of hunting ground, as he is entitled to hunt over almost any part of the 189,000,000 acres of National Forests, each hunter's individual share figuring out to over twelve acres—not quite Gardiner's Island but still quite a spot of land. There are also 90,000 miles of forest fishing streams and 1,500,000 acres of fishing lakes available to the fisherman. Thus every modern American outdoorsman is lord of his own piece of the democratic manor.

More in the American tradition than the private hunting estate idea, is the idealistic memory we have of our original frontiersmen like Daniel Boone, Davy Crocket, Buffalo Bill, and James Fenimore Cooper's fictional hero Natty Bumppo. Daniel, a fur trader and surveyor, enjoyed wilderness hunting and scouting. Davy, as you may remember from the TV theme song, was "king of the wild frontier" and a great bear hunter, as well as a congressman and hero of the Alamo. Buffalo Bill Cody, before becoming the head of a wild west show, hunted buffalo for the construction companies on the Great Plains. (Incidentally, if your husband wants to go all out in recapturing the experiences of the old West, he can apply to the U. S. Wildlife Service for permission to shoot one buffalo during the annual thin-out of the herds.)

Natty Bumppo, Cooper's hero of the *Leatherstocking Tales*, was a hunter who was brought up among the Delaware Indians. These five novels of frontier life follow Natty from his early days to old age, when at nearly ninety he was still a frontiersman. In each of them he helped defend some lovely young woman from attack or capture by unfriendly Indians. Your husband is not likely to run into any beautiful maidens in distress out in the woods, or Indians on the warpath, but it's something for him to dream about.

Don't think this is just romantic conjecture. We all like to have ties with the past. That is why many women collect antiques. If you enjoy attending country auctions or visiting the large auction galleries in the city to pick up fine old furniture, silver, glass, or ceramics, you are unconsciously keeping in touch with the old days and the old ways. You may turn a dry sink into a planter, make a coffee table out of a cobbler's bench, or put foam mattresses on authentic four-posters, but you are still clinging to your earlier heritage. Perhaps you are the sort of person who can't stand antiques and furnishes her home from stem to stern in Scandinavian Modern. But the primitive is ensconced in modern design. So you are simply going back even further in history than the collectors of Early-American antiques.

A TOUCH OF PHILOSOPHY

Love of the outdoors can produce for a man a profound emotional experience in its surroundings, and can make him think in a way that he doesn't ordinarily think. Architects, in designing the great cathedrals, can only imitate the patterns that are created by God and nature in the wilderness; and no organ ever built can recreate the music of the birds or the roar of the sea.

Fishermen catching salmon and steelhead trout in the Klamath River of northern California are just twenty miles from a Redwood grove where trees grow nearly as tall as the dome of St. Peter's Church in Rome, trees that have been in existence since biblical times. The rocks over which a hunter climbs are of even more ancient lineage. The sun and stars which guide him on his way—the poles that regulate his compass—were there when Moses took the children of Israel out of Egypt. The waters that are enjoyed by the fisherman are the same waters where first appeared the protoplasmic mass out of which evolved all creatures of the earth, including man, who is still 55 to 65 per cent water by weight.

St. Hubert, the patron saint of hunters, was converted

to Christianity while hunting over a thousand years ago, reportedly because he saw a stag with a luminous cross on its head.

The nickname for a hunter—Nimrod—comes from a character in Genesis, the great-grandson of Noah, described in the Bible as "a mighty hunter." Nimrod was a pretty important fellow in his day, and the capital of Assyria was named after him. One day in 1839, archaeologist Austen Layard was exploring Syria and Iraq; while floating down the Tigris on a raft with a friend, just as they were approaching a dam in the river, he noticed some odd-appearing, large mounds of earth. Their Arab boatman muttered some prayers to himself for a few moments and then sighed with relief, "Allah be praised!" When his passengers questioned him, he explained he had been thanking the Lord for getting him safely past "Nimrod's dam" and "Nimrod's mounds." The superstitious Arab explained further that Nimrod's mounds were all that was left of the once great city Nimrod had helped to build.

It took Austen five years to raise the money to return to the spot and excavate, but he finally got it from the British Ambassador in Istanbul. He and his assistants uncovered rooms lined with alabaster, embellished with carvings, and bearing ancient Assyrian writing. Later a statue was found of a winged animal with a human head, and the frightened diggers thought they had discovered Nimrod himself. Thirteen pairs of these winged lions and bulls were finally dug up, after their four-thousand-year burial, and these relics of the city of Nimrod the hunter now reside in the British Museum. If you and your husband visit London sometime, you can stop in and see them for yourselves.

There are many biblical references to fishing and fishermen, since fish have been the chief source of food from that time to this in the country of Israel. The first disciples of Christ were fishermen—Simon, Andrew, James, and John; and we all remember the famous admonition to them: "Follow me, and I will make you fishers of men."

Everyone has experienced some sort of mystical feeling when faced with the wonders of nature: the emergence of a butterfly from a cocoon, the flight of a bird, the rising and setting of the sun. Each season has its own wonders and miracles: the green leaves of spring, the flowers of summer, the flaming colors of autumn, and the soft snow-fall of winter. Many of our American author-naturalists have written of it—Joseph Wood Krutch, John Kieran, Henry David Thoreau. Brooks Atkinson, one-time drama critic of the *New York Times*, now writes lyrically of his experiences in his home in the Catskills. The most famous of these is Thoreau, who spent a year at Walden Pond in Massachusetts, away from civilization, to have an uninterrupted communion with nature.

Your sportsman husband could well understand Thoreau's injunction "Rise free from care before the dawn, and seek adventures," or his comment "Time is but the stream I go a-fishing in." He would certainly sympathize with his declaration "In wildness is the preservation of the world."

You yourself may or may not be an ardent nature lover. Perhaps you are a second Rachel Carson, to whom the sea around her was sufficiently exciting to inspire a full-length book, and whose worry over the possible extinction of natural wild life prompted another. Conversely, your interest in nature may be as dim as that of actress Gertrude Lawrence, who once inscribed in someone's autograph book, "Remember, dear Frances, that great elms from little acorns grow."

In any case, you don't need to be able to recognize and identify all the flora and fauna of the woods in order to appreciate, along with your husband, the awesome grandeur to which David referred in his 121st psalm when he said, "I will lift up mine eyes unto the hills, from whence cometh my help."

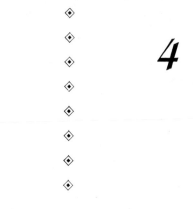

4

How Can His Outdoor Life Benefit You?

While reading the previous chapter you may have murmured to yourself, "It's all very well to go on about the physical, psychological, and philosophical benefits a sportsman gets from his hobby. But how about his wife? What's in it for her?"

There can be plenty in it for her. According to the Bureau of the Census, every person who engages in fishing and hunting spends six and a fraction days each year in that activity. Let's call it a week for a round number. So there you have it—a week's vacation from married life handed to you on a platter.

How your husband takes that week away from home varies, naturally. Some go out on six or seven separate single days a year. Others take three or four week ends. Still others take one full week at a whack. The extent of your vacation and temporary reversion to single blessedness depends on his whim: a half-dozen little happy holidays or a full week of unadulterated bliss.

Let's assume for the moment that you are getting a week end off. Sit down and think about what you would really most enjoy doing, or perhaps what job you would most enjoy getting done. Do you feel like:

- Hemming some dresses and making new curtains for the bedroom?
- Going on an outing with the family?
- Going somewhere with a woman relative or friend?
- Giving yourself a new hair rinse and complexion pack?
- Cooking and eating all the gooey, starchy messes you can think of?
- Taking up (seriously) a new sport to keep your figure in trim?
- Going on a crash diet to lose weight?
- Browsing through some museums and art galleries? Reading a good book?
- Shopping for a new dress or hat?
- Just slopping around in old wrapper and slippers and quietly doing nothing at all?

What the choice boils down to essentially can be put in three categories: self-indulgence, self-improvement, and independent recreation. We'll take them in that order.

YOU CAN BE SELF-INDULGENT

After he has kissed you goodbye, just turn over and go back to sleep and don't get up until ten o'clock. If you have a young child, then you'll need to feed it, change it, and put it in its crib or playpen before crawling back under the covers. If the children are teen-agers, they know how to take care of themselves. If they are in-between-agers, it is time they learned.

At ten, shuffle down to the kitchen in that rump-sprung old chenille bathrobe you've been meaning to throw away and never got around to doing. Beat yourself some waffle mix and cook up a batch of waffles in the electric waffle iron you've had since Christmas and never had time to use. Butter them liberally and pour plenty of genuine imitation maple syrup over them. Wash them down with two or three cups of real coffee—not instant, what's the rush?

Take your third cup of coffee then, and relax in front of the TV set. Watch a cooking program that gives you recipes for deviled crab, creamy macaroni salad, and peanut cinnamon wafers. Make a mental note to have this delectable meal for lunch, then switch to a travel show that takes you on an imaginary trip from Paris to the Riviera. Have lunch, take a refreshing nap, then back to the television set for a sports program. Lean back among the cushions with your feet on a hassock, munching on chocolate creams while tennis, track, and golf stars go through their grueling paces, straining and perspiring. Serve a dinner of canned hamburgers, ready-to-mash potatoes, and frozen string beans. Let the children wash the dishes while you put a stack of Sergio Franchi records on the stereo set, pick up a copy of an Agatha Christie, Mary Stewart, or Charlotte Armstrong mystery, and you're set for the evening. Come bedtime, pick yourself up and carry your paperback to bed with you, where you can continue to read until you have finished—without worrying about keeping your husband awake with the bed light.

If this program seems too energetic for you, just simmer it down to suit your own taste. Remember, of course, that unless you are the kind of woman who never gains a pound no matter how much she indulges herself, a few days spent like this will make it difficult for you to get into your girdle. When that point is reached, then it's time to go in for a little self-improvement.

YOU CAN TRY SELF-IMPROVEMENT

Self-improvement can be divided into two categories: physical and mental. Let's start with the physical.

If you'd like to cut down your weight, this is a good time to begin. A simple plan for moderate reduction consists of cutting out candy, desserts, and sugar-sweetened drinks, taking skim milk instead of whole milk, having no more than one slice of bread per meal, and rejecting second helpings of anything. After a couple of days on this régime, you will have grown accustomed to it and will be less likely to join your husband in an extra portion of meat and potatoes when he returns.

Exercise will also help keep your figure trim. It will stimulate your circulation as well, so that the color in your cheeks won't be all Max Factor or Helena Rubinstein. An hour's walk at a moderate pace will use up calories at the rate of two hundred per. Stretching is another simple, natural form of exercise. When you awake the first morning your husband is away, take a few minutes to relax completely before getting out of bed. Stretch your arms, legs, neck, and torso, to their fullest extent. Then relax completely, like a limp washcloth, loosening up each portion of your body separately from head to toe. Stretch once more, then relax, stretch, and relax.

After you get up and before you dress, you can pep yourself up further by standing with your hands on your shoulders, elbows resting at your sides. Jump your feet apart and fling your arms out sideways simultaneously; then return to the original stance. Repeat half a dozen times.

At night before you retire, you can do another simple exercise that will improve your posture. Stand with your back against a wall, your feet a few inches apart. Keep the chest high, draw in the abdomen, and roll the seat under tightly. Raise arms above the head, pressing fingers, elbows, and arms against the wall. Slowly drop your arms to the sides. Repeat half a dozen times.

If you want to exercise more strenuously, you can join a gym class or a dancing group, or take up some kind of sport. There are any number of suitable sports for women —riding, tennis, golf, bowling, swimming, skiing. Why not take one up along with one of the children?

After diet and exercise, next come the physical externals. Take the time one week end when your husband is away to try a new color rinse on your hair. Buy a fresh array of face creams and a different kind of make-up. We women sometimes get in an awful rut of using the same shade of powder, make-up base, rouge, eyebrow pencil, and lipstick for years because it was once becoming. A good rule to follow is to make the lipstick and rouge shades a little lighter as time goes by, and choose a powder color with a flattering hint of pink. The rouges and eyebrow darkeners that brush on are less harsh to the maturing face than the old-fashioned creams and pencils. Colored eye shadow and mascara are glamorous for evening, but too much eye make-up gives a hard effect for daytime wear.

The new creams, packs, and lotions rarely perform any of the miracles that are claimed for them; but they do have a psychological effect, and at least they get the skin good and clean. Soap cleansing cleans the skin too, and it is fine for the faces of men and children; but women who want to avoid its drying effects should stick to cold creams of one kind or another.

Home color rinses are all right for slight changes of color, where there is little or no grey present, and home permanents are okay for a few stray ends of hair or a little bang. But for a complete color change or a complete permanent, it is safer to depend on the beauty salon operator than on yourself.

A visit to the beauty parlor should perhaps come under the heading of self-indulgence, as well as self-improvement, for there is nothing more relaxing and uplifting than to put yourself in the hands of the experts and let them go to work. They can also give you valuable advice on hair styles and make-up choices, which you can follow at home between visits.

Well here you are, following a few week ends of dieting, exercise, and beauty aids. What next? Why clothes of course.

A few new brassieres will make an improved figure look

even better. Women are inclined to cling to the old brassiere long after it has lost its real usefulness and is just a limp shadow of its former self. The same is true of the girdle, although that item of clothing wouldn't be necessary if women exercised sufficiently to let their muscles do the work that Spandex is presently performing.

Next comes that staple item, the slip. It is a necessity for a smooth appearance except under a fully lined dress, suit, or skirt. Dacron is the best fabric, as it shrinks less than acetate and keeps its shape better than nylon. If your slips are tired-looking, get yourself a few well-made new ones. The stitching in knitted fabrics should be close and firm. Seams should be pinked and doublestitched or topstitched on woven materials, overcast on knitted fabrics. See that straps are sewed to the main body of the slip, not just to the trim. Half-slips should not have elastic attached. A zippered fitted half-slip with no elastic at all may cost a little more, but it will be worth the price.

While you're in the lingerie department, take a look at the lounging and sleepwear. You might find a nice sexy outfit that will make your husband glad he came home from the woods.

The choice of outer garments is a matter of personal taste and personal pocketbook, but there are some rules to keep in mind for the best-looking results if you decide to spend your husband's hunting or fishing week end on a shopping spree.

Remember that grey and beige are the best colors for a pale complexion, navy and black for a dark skin. Also, big women feel smaller in darker shades, and the thin one soon discovers that light colors add a little weight to her appearance. What if you are a brunette with a slim figure? Make your figure needs the primary consideration, and complement your skin tones with flattering accessories.

Fashion consultants say that all women but the very tall should pick clothes that accentuate their height. The really short woman looks better in dresses than suits and she will find long-waisted or empire styles flattering. The woman of average height should choose dresses or suits with slim skirts and lengthwise trim. The tall girl can go all out with suits and pleated skirts.

Jackets with hip pockets, dresses with peplums, and full skirts are the best choice for the thin-hipped figure. The heavier woman should avoid jackets that come down over the hips and wear skirts with a slim line and slight flair at the hem.

Choose a dress or suit that flatters your appearance and shows off your best points. If you have a slim waist, don't always hide it behind boxy jackets and shifts. If you have hips like the late Marilyn Monroe by all means avoid concealing full skirts. A woman with a round face can wear a V or other narrow neckline. The woman with a long face and neck usually looks most attractive with a high neckline. The square-faced type often looks best in oval necklines and off-centered pins on high, wide collars.

A new hat is the traditional pepper-upper for a woman's spirits, and its choice should have no rules or regulations about it. Pick the one that gives you the most lift. If you like big hats, choose a big one, even though you are only five feet tall and know you should be more discreet. If you've always stuck to tailored hats previously, try something fluffy and feminine for a change if that idea appeals

51

to you. Get away from basic black and practical navy and neutral brown or beige. Satisfy that secret yen for something in fire-engine red, bright orange, or an out-and-out heliotrope. Don't worry about whether or not your husband will like it. Save it to wear when you are out on your own and don't have to care about his likes or dislikes.

Now that we've taken care of the physical self-improvement, how about the mental side of things? Women usually dominate the cultural interests of the family, and their husbands often go along with them just to keep the peace. Wouldn't you enjoy a concert, ballet, art exhibit, or performance of Shakespeare a lot more if you didn't have someone beside you who was a trifle bored? Companionship is great, but why not go it alone for a change sometime when your husband is away? It will give you a chance to try something more exciting in the way of entertainment, since you won't have to make the usual compromise between what either of you would really like to see, ending up with something that is bland, inoffensive, and not particularly stimulating to anyone.

Another project you might get started with on your husband's days off in the wild is taking up an interesting hobby of your own. There are courses in writing, painting, musical instruments, arts and crafts, sewing and needlepoint, gardening, nature study, dramatics. You name it, and there will be someone teaching it—either at the local high school, college, or Y, or through private instruction or correspondence courses. Or you can take courses on television in comparative drama, classic and modern literature, science, art, and any number of languages. As with any other of these self-improvement projects, begin them when your husband is away and you have no distractions, and you have a better chance of gathering the necessary momentum for a habit that will carry on when he has returned.

INDEPENDENT RECREATION

There are other hobbies that are purely recreational, and only incidentally self-improving, like the collecting hobbies. You might start a coin or stamp collection, or a collection of bells, or old dolls, or rocks and shells, spending your husband's days away looking for additions to your collection, or setting it up more attractively. You might even tie in your collecting hobby with your husband's by collecting antique firearms or prints of hunting and fishing scenes. There are dealers in old guns all over the United States, and they can supply you with your chosen weapons and spare parts. Guns are sold at auction as well; but since you are probably not an expert, it is preferable to go to a dealer first and let him advise you. If you are an inveterate auction buff, go; but remember that you will not have much chance of outbidding the expert if the firearms on the block are worth anything at all. The sportsman collector usually wants his antique guns to be in usable working order, but you will probably just require something that you can display. Perhaps you visualize an old-time flintlock hung over your fireplace, or crossed dueling pistols in a decorative spot on the wall. (As with any guns, do not allow people to handle them, and keep them away from children.) Antique guns can cost from fifty to a hundred and fifty dollars, although rarities run higher in price.

A less expensive hobby is the collection of old prints.

Enjoying Life as a Sportsman's Wife

Your hunter husband will enjoy pictures of the chase, while your fisherman spouse will get a kick out of old-fashioned fishing scenes. Prints can be obtained from rare book shops, secondhand bookstores, antique stores, art shops, and galleries. Old prints are often advertised in magazines. Currier and Ives and Audubon prints are expensive, since their works have become standard; but there are thousands of other prints to be had from ten cents apiece on up. Two to five dollars should get you something worthwhile. Your best prints will make good wall decorations after they have been carefully framed. The rest of your collection should be kept in a special file, sorted by title and artist, and put into folders.

Suppose you want a more sociable recreation than collecting when the man of the house is not about? It's a very good idea. Call your best friend a week or two beforehand, and arrange to get tickets to some stimulating form of entertainment. If you live in a city, that's easy. There are always plays of one kind or another, from musicals to comedy to drama to way-out avant garde theater. If your residence is in the suburbs, plan to go into the nearest city for a day. Obtain a babysitter if necessary, and plan to go out on the town with one or more friends. Have lunch or dinner in some restaurant you've read about but never got around to visiting. Window-shop. See a show. Have an exotic after-theater snack.

If you have children who are sports fans, perhaps you would like to take them to see their favorite sports heroes perform. Their enthusiasm will spark your own enjoyment. And there are always ice shows, circuses, rodeos, puppet shows, and other entertainments that appeal to children as well as to adults.

A family picnic or other outing doesn't need to have Daddy along either. You can pack a lunch, put the kids in the car, and go if the weather is favorable. If it is chilly for picnicking, then a visit to the zoo, the natural history museum, or planetarium would be interesting. Out in the country there are all sorts of roadside amusements, from golf and archery ranges to carnivals. Then the children themselves are always full of suggestions.

Whatever you do while your husband is away, try not to make it anything noble—like spring or fall cleaning, or painting the pantry, or recovering the sofa, or weeding the lawn. Even though you don't say a self-righteous word, your husband may be made to feel guilty at having been out having a good time while you were at home "slaving."

Follow any of the suggestions in this chapter, and you will be much more relaxed, attractive, and revitalized when he returns. No matter how much he enjoyed himself while he was away, your husband will be pleased to find a wife waiting for him who is so very nice—and happy—to come home to.

◈
◈
◈
◈
◈
◈
◈
◈

5

What Does He Do for His Country?

◈
◈
◈

There is one important difference between the hunter and fisherman of yesterday and the sportsman of today. In the early days of this country's history the supply of land, water, and wildlife seemed so inexhaustible that forests were cleared, water was polluted, and game was slaughtered as though there were no tomorrow. If this had continued unchecked, none of the natural beauty of America would have remained for you and your family to enjoy.

It wasn't until a number of our wild animals had become totally extinct and others were facing extinction, that the government began to act. Forests and breeding grounds were snatched from destruction, and laws were passed limiting the catch of the outdoorsman. All this was to the sportsman's benefit, and he soon realized it. The duck stamp he purchases to attach to his hunting license produces two million dollars yearly to pay for refuge areas and the restoration of breeding and feeding marshes. The federal excise tax on arms and ammunition goes to aid the states in the wildlife preservation programs. In many states the money a man pays for his fishing license is used to support state fish hatcheries which replenish his supply. It seems like a paradox, but the hunter and fisher have joined hands with the conservationist.

HE PRESERVES ITS NATURAL RESOURCES

When you take your summer vacation, many of the parks you enjoy would not be there if it were not for the sportsman. In Massachusetts, large tracts that provide public hunting for birds and deer, and fishing for a variety of fish, also have natural facilities to take care of the outdoor recreation needs of the rest of the family. Surveys have shown that campers, picknickers, swimmers, bird-watchers, hikers, and berry-pickers make greater use of this land than the sportsman for whom it was intended.

As in all instances when man interferes with nature and tries to manage it to suit his needs, problems arise. One of the most important is overpopulation in certain areas of national parkland which are not used for hunting. A population explosion of elk and deer can result in starvation when there is not enough food to go around. Overbrowsing by big game animals can kill small trees, ruining their ranges and resulting in soil erosion and defacement of the landscape, as well as wildlife deaths through hunger and disease. The situation in Yellowstone Park was especially bad in recent years, and there was great debate over whether to leave the elk alone, have them shot by park service personnel, or allow public hunting in the park. This argument brought the problem to public attention and made people aware that wildlife in national parks must be managed, and the hunter can perform a public service by helping to control it.

As you drive through the country in your car and enjoy the refreshment of natural surroundings, you probably don't stop to think that they no longer happen by accident, but must be fought for. The outdoorsman is right up there among the foremost of the fighters. Thoughtless highway-builders and dam-constructors can change the entire face of the land. Highways are necessary, yes, but so are trout streams. Dams provide us with the power to run our washing machines, vacuum cleaners, and other labor-saving devices. They can also, if thoughtlessly situated, destroy our natural resources. The proposed Rampart Canyon Dam and Reservoir Project on the Yukon in Alaska will, if permitted to be completed, so block salmon-spawning runs that there will be a loss of catch of 200,000 to 400,000 fish annually. It will flood 7,000,000 acres of waterfowl nesting and growing area. The habitat for many moose, black bears, grizzly bears, and caribou will be eliminated.

You may think, "Well, that's too bad, all right, but it's so far away. I can't get alarmed over it." Closer to home for most of us, and examples of what can happen anywhere in the United States, are the threats of destructive highways, dams, and power plants, in New York, Maine, Montana, and elsewhere. According to the Montana Fish and Game Commission, "Montana is rapidly losing its trout stream fishing. Parts of naturally winding streams have been gutted and straightened to facilitate road and railroad construction, certain agricultural practices, and urban development."

The results of the rerouting of streams to your outdoorsman are a smaller production of trout—because food, shelter, and good clear water are no longer present. The results for you as an onlooker are that once-picturesque, winding streams are now as straight and uninspiring as canals. Engineers, because of the nature of their calling, are unwilling to let nature take its course; they would rather straighten out a stream than change the route of their road. As little boys they probably wanted Mother to rearrange the living room to accommodate their electric trains, and now they are getting even for her refusal.

The same thing that is happening in Montana is going on in New York, where the alteration of the Beaverkill-Willowemoc Rivers by road-builders will damage the trout production as well as the scenic value; and the construction of power plants in the Catskill area will deface the shores of the Hudson and inhibit wildlife.

As important a person as Justice William O. Douglas has complained of the destruction of the Allagash River and its environs in Maine. In *Field and Stream* (July, 1963) his article "Why We Must Save the Allagash" describes the beauties of its waters and its banks, where squaretail trout rise and moose feed on aquatic plants. Two dams under consideration at that time would turn the whole area into a lake, eliminating stream fishing and the present canoe-ways. The other alternative, new highways, would in Mr. Douglas' opinion bring too many tourists and commercialism, which would destroy its rustic attractions. Mr. Douglas would like to have seen the land, with its ash, maple, and birch forests and its deer, woodcock, and grouse populations, preserved as a wilderness waterway and hunting ground.

You and your husband should be on the alert for any signs of intended destruction in your area, and protest to your legislators about it. From a humanitarian view alone, the drowning of helpless animals and fledgling birds by the flooding from dams is undesirable, unless the need for power is urgent and the site in your neighborhood is the only one available.

If you have ever driven through rural France, perhaps on your way to Fontainbleau, you will have noticed that dotted through the farmers' fields were little corners of woodland. Seeing this occasional spot of green, with perhaps a bird gliding over it, makes the scenery more pleasing to your eye than endless squares of flat cultivation—and your husband will have made a mental note that there must be game thriving in these odd corners. He will have been right, and he and his fellow sportsmen, with the help of the U.S. government, are trying to convince the American farmer that he can do his bit for his country—and himself —by making his land produce useful wildlife.

Farmers' Bulletin No. 2035 of the U.S. Department of Agriculture explains to the farmer how he can have a better farm or ranch by having wildlife on his land. As the bulletin explains, if there are not enough rabbits on his land to feed the foxes in the neighborhood, the foxes may turn to domestic fowl for food. If there are too few foxes to eat meadow mice, the mice will consume the alfalfa intended for his dairy cows. If there are not enough birds, there may be too many destructive insects, and a resultant shortage of grain for beef cattle. Also, there must be useful insects to pollinate alfalfa, red clover, and sweet clover so that they will produce seed. The bulletin also tells him of the sport and food that can be provided for himself and his friends by the encouragement of a game bird and mammal population on his grounds, as well as a fish population in his ponds. A lovely little wooded, grassed, and hedged pond area provides bass, bluegills, channel catfish, and trout for the fisherman; and a wood duck nest box can bring in some nesting ducks. Native shrubs improve the appearance of bare wire fences and offer wildlife cover. Living fences and contour hedges look attractive, and they save both soil and game. Legume-grass field borders control erosion and harbor useful wildlife.

HE PROTECTS ITS WILDLIFE FROM POLLUTION

All in all, you can see how your sportsman's interests help keep the land around you a pleasanter and more desirable place in which to live. They also keep it a safer place in which to live. The deadly chemical sprays which kill off insects near American and Canadian streams, and leave nothing for young salmon to eat, are the bane of the salmon fisherman there. They also endanger human beings who come in contact with them. You will remember when contaminated cranberries were taken off the market because they had been sprayed with a weed killer suspected of causing cancer. When sage is killed off by sprays to produce more grasslands for cattle to range in Illinois, moose and beaver are driven away for lack of food—because the spray also kills the willows which they eat. Then the dams the beaver made fall into disuse, so that the trout do not thrive and waterfowl are no longer attracted to the region. This is hard on the hunter and fisherman. And on everyone else. When your air, water, and food contain residues of these sprays, it is a threat to the health of your entire family.

Because of the influence of the sportsman and other conservationists, as well as the widespread publicity attendant on Rachel Carson's *Silent Spring* (Houghton Mifflin, 1962), industry has been investigating safer methods of killing pests like rats, moths, beetles, and all the rest of the common nuisances. Researchers at McNeil Laboratories in Fort Washington, Pennsylvania, have discovered a cheap compound called "norborene," which kills rats by constricting their blood vessels but spares cats, dogs, and human beings. At the University of California in Los Angeles, entomologist Roy Pence discovered a new technique for killing moths and beetles. Instead of using old-fashioned pesticides, he can save your rugs and clothes from attack by spreading the material in them with compounds called "anti-metabolites"—which, as their name indicates, upset the insects' metabolism until they sicken and die from malnutrition. This type of compound is non-toxic to human beings. As experiments like these progress, we shall, hopefully, end up with sprays that will kill the undesirable insects while sparing the insects that birds and fish feed on, and kill undesirable vegetation while leaving that which is valuable to animals.

You will want to join your husband in the fight for the use of less lethal sprays, as well as that for the control of unwanted insects by sterilization and the introduction of insect-eating birds and animals. Nobody wants to be over-run with swarms of flies, mosquitoes, and gnats; but the life of a child is worth a little discomfort. There is not much point in telling a teen-ager of the dangers of inhaling cigarette smoke, when he is being exposed to chemicals and other pollutants just by breathing the air around him.

The river waters that become so polluted that your husband can no longer catch fish in them have become dangerous places for children to swim. These pollutions can be the result of wastes from chemical plants, untreated sewage, or even the detergent you use in your wash. Ask your supermarket salesman for the new detergents being put out, which will not pollute the waters in your neighborhood with those sudsy puffs you may have seen floating around. Nobody wants to poison his own well, and the detergent manufacturers have worked hard to perfect a product which will not have undesirable wastes.

Another industry which is looking out for your welfare and your husband's, as well as its own, is the forestry industry. Lumber mills used to lay waste to the country, depriving sportsmen of hunting and fishing grounds and defacing the scenic beauty of the land. Now concerns like the Weyerhaeuser Company in Washington, call them-selves "tree farmers." They have discovered that forests are a renewable natural resource. Through wise conserva-tion and replanting, they keep their own business going while at the same time providing places where Americans can hunt, fish, and enjoy the beauties of nature. Their timber holdings in Washington, Oregon, California, New Hampshire, North Carolina, Mississippi, Alabama, and Canada provide wonderful outdoor refuge areas for elk, bobcats, raccoons, foxes, blacktail deer, ducks, and geese; and salmon and other fish are abundant in the pure water provided by these forest lands. At the same time, the house you live in may be made of its structural products and the interior decorated with its plywood and hardwood panels, its architectural doors, furniture, and cabinets. The book or magazine you read and the paper you write a letter on, as well as the carton containing your milk, may have come from the wood fibers of a tree grown on a farm where your husband can hunt and fish. Even your car may have parts made of its molded wood fibers.

SOMETIMES HE GOOFS

At this point, the praise of your husband as "nature's nobleman"—influencing his country to preserve its wilderness areas, and farmers to make their land more attractive, and chemical sprayers to act with more caution—may begin to feel out of proportion. Surely he isn't all that sweetly reasonable?

Well, in a word, "No." In many instances he opposes the government's creation of national parks because hunting is sometimes prohibited on parkland—with the result that the park is not created, and the land is cut up into building lots, made into factory sites, or destined for other less attractive uses like dams, highways, and power plants. Often when it is too late, he realizes that if he had joined with those fighting for the park, the wild natural area would have been preserved; and later, as animal life multiplied, he might have been offered the opportunity to hunt or fish on the land after all.

The sportsman sometimes finds himself in conflict with the farmer because some among sportsmen are lacking in hunting and fishing etiquette and in respect for land-owner's rights; so the farmer retaliates with stronger tres-pass laws. Thoughtless urban dwellers turned sportsmen sometimes disregard common courtesies, do not understand farm problems, and lose the good will of the landowners. This is rather shortsighted, since small game wildlife habi-tats are shrinking on the six million farms and ranches. Hunters and fishermen with the longer view will want to regain the friendship of the farmers and ranchers, so that the latter will be encouraged to increase game crops on their lands rather than making them barren of game.

The careless or incompetent hunter antagonizes the wild-life departments by leaving wounded animals and winged birds to die lingering deaths. Each year, according to the Canadian Wildlife Department, thousands of Canadian geese die in this way from wounds inflicted by hunters unable to retrieve birds they wing and bring down.

The sport fisherman often comes into disagreement with the commercial fisherman over the use of salt water fishery resources. There are about ten million anglers who fish in salt water, and the number is expected to double in the 1970's. Despite the millions of fish in the sea, there is a limit to their number, and there will soon not be enough of some species to satisfy both sport and commercial interests. Marine fishery scientists suggest that in a starving

65

world no one should be allowed to fish whose catch is not intended to be eaten—like the man who poses with his large game fish for a picture to be sent to the home town paper, or the man who is only interested in a mounted trophy. The outdoorsman retorts with the suggestion that some commercial fishermen are guilty of far greater waste, when they neglect to use the type of fishing gear which would allow the escape to sea of young fish of most species to grow and propagate themselves. As for the people who consume the products of the commercial fisheries, the sportsmen often say, in paraphrase of Marie Antoinette, "Let 'em eat meat!"

The final solution to this problem will be up to the government and the Bureau of Sport Fisheries and Wildlife. It has been suggested that a three-dollar license fee for marine fishing would supply the necessary finances for special studies of the problem, just as licensing of fresh-water fishermen has provided the money for management of fish in inland waters. The sportsman with an eye to the future will be glad to pay to see that his favorite recreation is insured.

HE CONTRIBUTES TO ITS ECONOMY

We have seen how the outdoorsman contributes to the preservation of the country's beauty. He also makes a great contribution to its economy. The purchase of goods and services utilized in fishing on marine waters alone amounts to over six hundred million dollars yearly at retail, and it is expected to double that amount in the 1970's. The entire fishing population of this country spends around three billion dollars a year on goods and services. The hunters spend another billion dollars, for a total of four billion dollars, which is big business in anybody's language.

Don't let all this give you an inferiority complex, though. Women's yearly expenditures for their clothing now contribute to a ten-billion-dollar industry employing 367,000 people. They also keep 271,623 hairdressers and cosmetologists busy each year making them pretty, and 10,000 furriers and 43,000 jewelers occupied producing glamorous furs and baubles for them to wear. If this isn't contributing to the national economy, I don't know what is. As for the preservation of the country's beauty, women are a living part of that beauty, and the more they spend on keeping themselves attractive, the more attractive they—and the country as a whole—will be.

If you and your sportsman each keep on doing your part, this country will continue to be "America the Beautiful" in more ways than one.

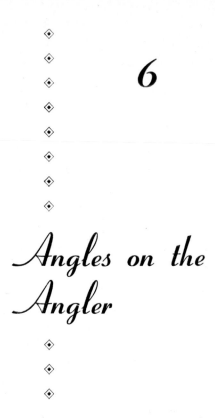

6

Angles on the Angler

There are probably about thirty million fishermen in this country, including the seventeen million who have licenses, plus all those who are under age or who fish in salt water where licenses are not always required. If you occasionally join your husband on a fishing jaunt, your understanding of its attractions for him will depend on your own enthusiasm for the sport. If you have never fished, its appeal may be a complete mystery.

Over ten thousand books have been published telling of fishing experiences and the benefits to be derived from them, the most famous being Izaak Walton's *The Compleat Angler*. Back in 1655, Mr. Walton made a statement that your fisherman husband might easily repeat today: "I have laid aside business, and gone a-fishing."

Essentially, that seems to be the reason men go fishing, so that they can lay aside the daily routine and escape to a place where the mind can be refreshed in an inspiring atmosphere.

What else a man gets out of fishing besides refreshment and relaxation depends on his individual tastes and capacities. If he is a loner, he can fish entirely by himself and enjoy it. If he likes company, he can arrange to fish with as many companions as he wishes. The muscular man can pick the kind of fishing that requires physical exercise; the sluggish fellow can fish with hardly any exertion at all.

STARTING WITH THE BAIT

There is more to fishing than going out to a favorite spot, throwing in a line, and waiting for something to bite. A man must have the proper equipment and the bait that he thinks will work best for the fish he is after. There is a myth that has been circulating for as long as there have been fishermen—about the boy with a length of string and a bent pin with a piece of red flannel on it, catching more fish than his adult rivals with their expensive tackle and carefully selected bait. And there may be something to it at that, for a man never knows what kind of bait, if any, will lure the fish he wants. Out in San Francisco's Lake Merced one summer, some anglers used miniature marshmallows for bait and found that the trout loved them. A catfish has reportedly been caught with a frankfurter, while at Douglas Reservoir in Tennessee fishermen have caught big catfish on trotlines strung with baitless hooks. It is said that this attraction to the metal hooks may have been due to a mineral deficiency in the water, but that sounds a little like a fish story to me. As Don Marquis once said, "Fishing is a delusion entirely surrounded by liars in old clothes."

If your husband likes to use night crawlers for bait, you know that some warm, damp night in spring will find him out on the local baseball field or golf course with a flashlight, collecting these big fishing worms. They are the favorite of cane-pole fishermen; but the bass or trout fisherman will also sometimes use them instead of the artificial lure, when that doesn't seem to be working. Crawfish are another good bait for bass and almost any other kind of fish. So are minnows and young dobson flies. Catfish usually go for smelly bait, since they have a sensitive sense of smell. If you get tired of finding worms in a box under the sink, crawfish in the refrigerator, and the overripe odor of catfish bait everywhere, you might suggest to your husband that he try marshmallows or frankfurters or baitless hooks. Or you may induce him to shift to artificial lure and fly fishing.

Fly fishing is the preferred way of catching trout, and the flies are constructed to resemble vaguely some adult or immature insect the trout likes to eat. There are also flies to catch salmon, bass, panfish, and others. The flies themselves can become an interesting off-season hobby for the angler who wants to create his own with the proper fibers, feathers, and silk. So if you see your husband eyeing your new wig covetously, or hear a suspicious yelp from the family poodle, you'll understand why.

Flies can be bought ready made for the man who has not the time or deftness to make them himself. They have been used in England and the United States since the fifteenth century, and their very names are quaint and romantic-sounding: The Royal Coachman, The Silver Doctor, The Queen of the Waters, Rio Grande King, Western Bee, Pink Lady, Mormon Girl, Cut Throat, Barber Pole, The McGinty, The Professor, and The Paramachene Belle are among the favorite flies still in use in the United States.

HOOK, LINE, AND . . .

The fly is constructed right on the hook to be used, for after all the hook is the most essential unit in sport fishing, dating back more than two thousand years. The lake dwellers of Switzerland used an early form of it fashioned of bronze, found by archaeologists, who say these people probably fished conveniently off their back porches. Hooks were developed all over the world by the Egyptians, the American Indian, and the Polynesians—made of shell, bones, stone, and other materials from thorns to insect legs. The volume production of fish hooks came in England and Scandinavia in the steel era, when needle manufacturers went in for fish hooks as a sideline. In the present century American know-how has turned out the hook with the hollow ground point and so-called "Eagle Claw," made of a precise formula and precision tempering. They come in all sizes, but the rule seems to be to use the smallest size hook that is practicable.

Above the hook comes the part of the line called the "leader," sometimes made of braided wire to withstand stress and strain. At one time the leader was made of braided horse hair, at another of braided raw silk. There is a material derived from the silkworm, just before it spins its cocoon, called "silkworm gut," which has been used for many years and is still in use for this purpose. Luckily for the poor silkworms, who are pulled apart and their sacs emptied of a fluid which hardens on exposure to the air, to produce this gut, nylon is being developed into even finer leader material.

Next comes the line itself, made of silk for many years, enameled to make it easier to control. Silk, enameled fly and casting lines are still used today, although they also come in nylon. They are woven round for fly fishing and squarish for casting. The square line is said to wind on the spool in flatter layers and to cut down on tangles and the accompanying profanity.

In the simplest method of fishing, the line is merely attached to the end of a cane or bamboo pole. This is called "jig fishing." For convenience in pulling in the fish, the reel was invented as an improvement on this method. The single-action reel (called at that time a "wind" or "wheele") is mentioned in Walton's *Compleat Angler*, and its description is very similar to today's counterpart. George Snyder of Paris, Kentucky, invented an improved reel with a spool which would release the line as it was cast. He was a watchmaker, and his first reels were made in his shop for himself and his friends. Later the Meek Brothers, two other watchmakers, went in for reel production commercially. The Meek product was like most of today's multiplying reels, the spool on which the line was wound revolving four times for every turn of the reel handles. This reduced the resistance of the spool during the cast, making it possible to cast farther and more accurately. The early reels had jeweled bearings in them, just like a watch. Today the bearings are made of alloys, which are cheaper and more service- able. There have also been automatic reels developed, equipped with springs that wind up the line as it is payed out and stationary spool reels, in which the spool remains stationary as the line goes out. If all this sounds pretty complicated and you'd rather stick to jig fishing with a cane pole, a cotton line, and worm on a hook, I don't blame you. However, these very complications are what add to the fascination of the hobby for men, since they delight in gadgetry.

THE FISHING ROD

His rod is the next item on the list of necessary tackle. When it just has a line fastened to it and is used to haul in a fish directly, it is called a "pole." But when it can be used to play the fish before pulling it in, it attains status and is known as a "rod." A casting or fly rod may be made of split bamboo, steel, or glass—with glass today's most popular choice. A variety of woods were used for rods in the first half of the nineteenth century, lancewood, paddlewood, ironwood, cedar, and hickory being among those employed for the purpose. By the 1880's, American anglers had begun to prefer the light, flexible bamboo rod, made from cane grown in the Tonkin province of China. So attached were they to this type of rod that many of them clung to it long after the advent of the steel rod. When the glass rods finally came along, they did catch on—not so much because men had lost their nostalgic attachment to the old-fashioned bamboo, but for the more practical reason that the supply of Chinese bamboo to the western world was limited.

PLUG CASTING

Now we've covered bait, flies, hooks, lines, and rods, and you'd think that would be all. But there's more! For bait casting there are wood, metal, or plastic lures called "plugs" or "spoons," which are supposed to fool the fish into thinking they are its natural food. Since they usually have three hooks on them, he is a goner no matter where he strikes the lure. Whether the fish thinks the lures are food or not is by that time an academic question.

The spoon is a shining lure invented over a hundred and fifty years ago by a man in Vermont named Julio Buel. He is said to have accidentally dropped a spoon over the side of his boat while fishing in Lake Bomoseen and seen a fish rush at it as it spun and wobbled to the bottom. Anyone who has ever owned a parakeet knows the attraction of anything bright and shiny, and fish evidently have the same sort of reaction, which accounts for the popularity of the spoon-spinner and spoon-wobbler bladed lures developed by Buel and later manufacturers. The plug type of lure has more body to it, and got its name in an equally logical way—because the early plugs were whittled plugs of wood. According to fishing legend, a man named James Heddon was walking along a creek, whittling to pass the time, and he tossed the wood he had whittled into the water. A big bass leaped for it, and the plug lure was born! Heddon went into the lure business, and his company still manufactures the #210 lure. Today's plugs look like little fish and some have propeller attachments.

Bait casting is still a popular kind of fishing in this country; so with his casting tackle all ready, your fisherman is all set to go out and catch his share of fresh-water game fish. Although fishing is a year-round sport, you may have noticed that May and June seem to be the most popular months. This is because the fish are then finished with nesting and spawning, when they've been too busy to eat very much, and they are all very hungry. Your husband is not the only fisherman aware of this situation, so there are not only more fish to be caught at this time of year but also more fishermen out trying to catch them. To compete successfully with one another, the fishermen need to be able to cast their bait into distant spots to cover as much water as possible. Casting enables the sportsman to fish in shallow water without frightening the fish away with his shadow. It helps him to catch that elusive fish behind a rock or log—he hopes!

You may not have thought of your husband as a particularly graceful man; but if he is to be successful at bait casting, his wrist must be as flexible as that of a ballet dancer. He grasps the rod with thumb on top and then turns his wrist to the left so that the reel crank is on top and his thumb at the side. Then he aims in the desired direction, with forearm extended slightly upward and elbow close to his body, lowering the rod as he sights his target. The rod is then lifted straight upward, using only wrist action, and pushed down again with hand and wrist movements alone, while the thumb pressure on the reel spool is released. The rod tip is lowered straight ahead, in line with the arm, thumb again on spool to prevent a backlash. These movements, to be done correctly, take as much practice as a bowling delivery or a golf swing, so don't object to his practicing out in the back yard. Just request a little advance notice, so you can corral the children and warn the immediate neighbors.

FLY CASTING

Fly fishing requires a rather heavy line, with the lightweight fly at the end of the leader, since the weight of the line casts the lure. The line is cast back and forth, with a little more line being let out each time in order to obtain distance. The fly on the end of the line is one of the thousands already developed and being innovated every year. There are wet flies which sink when they hit the water, resembling a drowned or underwater insect, and dry flies which float like live insects. A fly rod can also be used with crickets and grasshoppers as bait, to catch pan fish. Then there are the longer, fuller flies called "streamers," which are good for catching bass. These flies are very colorful and attractive, and a woman's first thought on seeing them is that they would make a fine trimming for a summer beach hat.

Fly casting is similar to bait casting, except that the forearm is used along with the wrist, and twenty to thirty feet of line is stripped off and held in the left hand at the start. After the lift of the rod and the forward cast, the line in the left hand is released. The left hand is used to strip more line from the reel, or to take in the line from the water. There are all sorts of fly-casting tricks to be learned to get a good high backcast and then to cast the line forward in such a way that the second cast is longer than the first and closer to the desired target. Theoretically the backcast is not supposed to get caught in the nearby trees or shrubbery. That sort of thing only happens to women and amateurs, to hear the fishermen tell it.

SPIN CASTING

Spin casting, now rapidly replacing bait casting, has the advantage of making it possible to cast lighter lures greater distances. If your sportsman fishes in spots where the fish are shy and suspicious, then distance is important to him. In the spinning reel, the spool doesn't revolve when you cast; the line is pulled from the end of the spool by the weight of the lure. Since there are no moving parts to this type of reel, you should be aware, if you are familiar with physics, that there is a minimum of resistance to the cast. It is supposed to have been devised originally by a fisherman who worked in a linen mill, where the thread was stripped from the spindles in the same way. A very light line can be used in this method of fishing, and it offers little backward pull as it zips through the air for seventy-five feet or more. Spinning lures are similar to bait-casting lures but weigh two to three-eighths of an ounce less. Live baits can also be used, as they will be cast long distances without injury, and will have freedom to move about in the water.

The "Simon-pure" European-born form of spin fishing rose to popularity in this country with the use of open-faced spinning reels designed to mount below rather

77

than above the rod handle, much in the fashion of fly reels. Noticing at once the advantages of these reels, American manufacturers almost immediately began spewing forth a vast and confusing number of reels having little in common with them but the stationary spool. Whether open- or closed-faced, reels during the last decade have been made to mount only on top of the rod, some only below the rod; and there are many now that can be used either above or below the rod, at the whim of the fisherman. With nearly any one of them, women and kids can cast fishing lures as easily and as well as men, and with no tangled lines to spoil the fun.

In spin casting, the movement is all done with the wrist and forearm. Practice casting with a hookless casting weight will improve the fisherman's skill and timing.

With the reel mounted below the rod, the line is held below but against the rod by the fisherman's right index finger. He lifts the rod and lowers it in a swift arc, releasing the line with his index finger as he casts. To stop the outgoing line, he presses his index finger along the edge, side, or front of the spool (depending on the particular reel), engaging the line with his finger. If his reel has a closed rather than open face, he may have to brake the outgoing line by slightly advancing the reel handle. For left-handed fishermen the same kind of reel is available with features reversed.

With the kind of spin-casting reel that is mounted on top instead of beneath the rod handle, the procedure is very similar to that of ordinary bait casting. This kind of reel requires only the pressure of the user's finger on a control plate mounted on top of the reel and depressed by the thumb to brake, stop, or lock the line. Releasing the plate frees the line in casting.

Except for the easier handling of lightweight lures and the greatly diminished probability of a tangled line in spin casting, the similarity to bait casting is evident. In fact, when equipped with a somewhat stronger line, most spin-casting reels will handle the heavier lures for which the original form of bait-casting reel was designed.

Spinning is said to bring in the big ones, so all that practice should have some results that your husband can brag about to friends and neighbors.

Fishing from a boat is fun. The sportsman can cover more ground, and he can get to the deep water where fish go to keep cool in hot weather. One boating method is called "trolling," and it consists of towing bait or lure behind the boat with a linen or nylon line, for ordinary use, or a wire line which will sink and carry the bait to greater depths. Float fishing means just what it sounds like. The fisherman lets the current carry his boat downstream, and he fishes as it floats along. Jugging is another way of fishing from a boat base. The line is tied to a can or jug, or anything which floats high. The hooks are baited and the cans or jugs tossed into the water. The fisherman relaxes in the boat, lunching and getting a suntan, while the fish proceed to catch themselves. When the jugs start to jiggle, he knows he's either fallen asleep or really caught some catfish.

BOTTOM FISHING

The most popular type of salt-water fishing is called "bottom fishing." This type of fishing requires little in the way of tackle. A line, hook, and sinker are sufficient for catching smaller fish, although a rod and reel can be used to catch the large fishes, such as a shark or grouper. A one-time Caribbean dictator used to maintain that it was sissified to use rods and reels in bottom fishing, and he demonstrated his theory by landing hundred-pounders with just a line and hook. Other sportsmen can imitate this feat at their own risk.

The reason bottom fishing is practiced so commonly is that anyone can casually stand on a pier, bridge, causeway, or dock and drop his bait, and—with luck—catch a fish or two. There are specialists in this type of fishing, as in all others, who study the different localities and their conditions, the kinds of bottom, the prevalence of bait fishes and other natural foods, the phases of the moon and the tides, and every other guide but astrology charts. This makes good sense, since the fisherman who knows where the fish are is likely to have the largest catches. Like any other creatures, they congregate where the best food and shelter are available, in rocky or grassy areas and around old wrecks, pilings, piers, and jetties. These provide shelter, and the marine life attached to them provide meals. The serious student of bottom fishing will get maps of the bottoms which are printed by the federal government and sold at most marine hardware stores. These indicate the depth of the water, the type of bottom, and the locations of wrecks and other obstructions.

Once he has picked his spot and prepared his tackle, the fisherman has to choose his bait from innumerable possibilities. Salt-water fish show good taste in food and are fond of many of the delicacies we human beings enjoy. They particularly like clams, either the soft-shell variety that we prefer steamed or the hard-shell kind that we eat on the half-shell under the name of Cherrystones or Little Necks. They also go for appetizers like herring, crabs, shrimp, and sardines, not to mention squid and eels.

SURF FISHING

Surf fishing is similar to fresh-water casting and spinning but a bit more strenuous. The equipment is heavier, and hip boots or waders are worn, along with a belt and socket in which the rod fits. The cast is made not only by the wrists and arms but by the shoulders as well, plus the entire weight of the body from the toes up; and both hands are used in making the cast. Some surf fishermen say they can catch fish only on the incoming tide, and others swear by the outgoing; so whichever your husband's belief may be, he has plenty of company. Surf fishermen catch channel bass, barracuda, yellowtail, bluefish, striped bass, and weakfish, among others.

Sharks can be caught by surf fishing, for those who want to make an impressive catch. Sharks weighing from one hundred to two hundred pounds are pulled in not far from Boynton Beach in Florida and Jones Beach on Long Island. At Monterey Bay, California, near San Francisco, shark derbies are held twice a year for six hours, and during that time two thousand pounds of shark may be reeled in! If your husband brings home a shark and your Betty Crocker cookbook doesn't give you a recipe for shark steak, you'll have to improvise, or else advise him to go have it stuffed.

Fortunately for the cook, casting for bass and other more commonplace fish is even more popular. Striped bass are such a favorite with surfers that in 1879 they were shipped by rail all the way from the Navesink River in New Jersey out to California, so that they could be introduced to the West Coast for the benefit of fishermen out there. Surf fishing can become so obsessive that barbers leave their chairs and psychiatrists desert their couches to rush down to the beaches for the summer run of bass.

Whether he owns his own yacht, rents a boat for the day, or goes out on a party boat or charter boat, your salt-water fisherman will sometimes want to get away from the shore and out in the deep water, where the really sporty fish live. He can troll for bluefish, channel bass, and stripers, the same fish he can catch from the surf; but his ambition will be to get out deeper, where he can troll for big game fish such as marlin, tarpon, and sailfish—and come back to the dock to have his picture taken with his mighty prize. Fighting and capturing a big fish will give him such a sense of power that he will probably be difficult to live with for weeks afterward; but it will do him a world of good, so bear with it.

THE ANGLES ARE NUMEROUS

As you can see, fishing has something for everybody from the quiet, contemplative angler, with little muscular development to the forceful aggressive type with muscles to spare. A fisherman can live inland or at the shore. He can follow his sport in June if he likes the relaxation of mild weather, or in January if he prefers the stimulation of snow and ice. Fishing is the sport of presidents and philosophers, writers and businessmen, the rich man on his forty-foot yacht and his less affluent brother in a stubby canoe. All of them derive equal joy from their hobby. And their wives can be happy to have them busy with an avocation that is so restful and invigorating compared to most other diversions a man might have.

♦
♦
♦
♦
♦
♦
♦
♦

7

Hints on the Hunter

♦
♦
♦

The attraction of the hunt to a sportsman is something like the attraction of an open fireplace for the rest of us. A fireplace is as much of an anachronism in the age of thermostats and automatic heat as hunting in the age of the meat packing plant and chain store. Yet a burning fire on the hearth gives us a sense of warmth and security that we never get from modern heating systems, because it stimulates our senses in an age-old way. And hunting gives a man the ancient feeling of being the strong family provider, even though his trips to the office every morning are what actually produce the food, clothing, and shelter you need.

There is variety in hunting, just as there is in fishing, and the particular sport that appeals to one man may not be the favorite of another. The weapon is usually the same—a gun—although there have been revivals of archery, falconry, and even slingshots, in recent years. There are big game hunters and small game hunters, predator hunters and small-mammal hunters, upland game bird hunters, shorebird hunters, and waterfowl hunters. Some hunt with shotguns, others with rifles, some with bow and arrow and others with handguns. There are men who hunt alone, and there are men who like the companionship and assistance of a dog for pointing, flushing, and retrieving. Grouse can be hunted either with or without the help of a dog. A fast, aggressive dog will flush grouse too quickly, and the grouse will be off and out of shooting range before the hunter can shoot him. An older, slower dog will work more closely with his master; and the gentle, manageable setter is often the choice for this particular sport.

The grouse hunter—like his dog, if he has one—must be patient and deliberate. The bird's protective coloration makes him blend in with the scenery, so that the hunter must be observant. It is not necessary for the sportsman to enjoy the beauty of nature; but if he does, he gets an extra bonus when hunting game like grouse, which live in lovely natural surroundings in the wilds of Canada and much of the northern belt of the United States. The grouse is such a regal bird, with his ruffed neck and fan tail, that the hunter who bags him feels that he shares some of that regality. This too is part of the fascination of hunting—making the ultimate connection with some such grand and beautiful creature at the split second of the kill. The feeling is perhaps similar to what Hemingway described in bullfighting as "the moment of truth."

Hunting isn't all philosophy and grandeur, as you know. It is also a test of wits between the instincts of the elusive game and the more highly evolved brain of man. Most often, though, hunting is a lot of fun, especially with the companionship of another man or group of men, with whom to share experiences. When the trip lasts several days, there are also the evenings in which to sit around and rehash the day's adventures.

In modern times, men are so surrounded and overwhelmed by femininity from birth to death that they welcome the company of other men. The little boy is supervised by Mom and educated in the elementary and high school grades primarily by women teachers. He grows up to be surrounded by coeds at college and a female work force in the office; then he marries a woman—naturally—and spends most of his time with her in his leisure hours. No wonder he welcomes a chance for bull sessions in old clothes and a growth of beard! Some wives may suspect that hunting is just an excuse to get away from the bogey of female domination; but that's not quite true either. If it were, why go to all that trouble? The husbands could just slip out to the local bowling alley or billiard emporium and get the same relief.

THE EXPENSES INVOLVED

While it is not necessary to spend more than the average eighty dollars or so a year on the sport, the possibilities for impressive spending are limitless. It is interesting to note that although the $50,000,000 spent in maintaining hunting and fishing areas in this country sounds like a lot of money, eighty times that amount is spent in catching fish and killing game. If it is difficult for you to understand how sportsmen can possibly spend all that money unless they use it to light their cigars and pipes, or hang it in the bushes as bait, here is an idea of some of the tools of the trade it might be possible for an outdoorsman to use:

Say, for instance, he's out after ducks lighting in the center of a big beaver pond. To get out there he needs an aluminum canoe or a duck boat, and to attract the ducks he needs some decoys. After setting the decoys and hiding the canoe, he then needs chest-high waders, and probably a duck blind.

An important item on the hunter's list of accessories is a pair of binoculars. These can cost as little as twenty-five dollars or as much as two hundred dollars. The investment pays off, since a distant deer that looks like a doe to the naked eye can be discovered to be wearing antlers through a good pair of 6X glasses.

Sportsman Harold F. Blaisdell, in *Field and Stream* Magazine (November, 1961), lists the following as the absolute minimum in hunting tools, and I quote:

• Dogs for native birds and game
• Open-bored shotgun for upland game

- Full-choke shotgun for ducks and varmints
- Decoys
- Fabric boot-footed waders
- Hip boots
- Deer rifle
- Binoculars
- Snowshoes
- Boots and clothing for fall hunting
- Ditto for winter hunting
- Small items, including compass, knife, and matchsafe

Mr. Blaisdell adds that the above has not included many other essentials, like dog collars, tie-out chains, kennels, leashes, canoe paddles, anchors, ropes, game bags, packsacks, patching materials, etc. There are many other pieces of equipment that even Mr. Blaisdell doesn't mention—such as a clay pigeon catapult or a sharpshooter's sighting-in bench, to keep the shooting eye sharp between seasons; a space heater for hunting shacks; 'scope sight for hunting rifles; a duck boat, a rifle sling, a gun cabinet, a duck blind, and so on and on and on. Since hunting seasons are limited by law, all this gadgetry keeps a man busy in off-season either building his own, if he's a do-it-yourselfer, or shopping for it if money is no object.

THE FAVORITE GAME BIRDS

Dogs are widely used in hunting birds like partridge, pheasant, and quail. They point the bird and get it into the air within range of the hunter's gun so that his shot makes a clean kill, which is humane to the animal and avoids the waste of a wounded bird that hides itself in an undetectable spot to die. A sportsman can get pretty frustrated when three or four pheasants out of every ten hide from him under a pile of leaves or down a badger hole. It's not likely to make the pheasants very happy either.

With wild turkey, there are turkey-calls to lure the unsuspecting birds—and to give the sportsman yet another gadget to buy or make. One call is made by putting a wooden peg upright in half a coconut shell, then scraping a piece of slate across the peg. There are also box calls, in which a piece of chalked slate is scraped across the edge of the box, or a bevel on the underside of the cover engages the lips of the box.

The common method of hunting turkey is to flush them and then wait for their return at daylight. One old method is to roost the turkey and then stalk him at twilight. The trouble with this is that they roost in pines or other evergreens, or in mossy trees, making them difficult to spot in the dusk. This leads to hunters shooting at bunches of mistletoe or squirrels' nests instead of the turkey, with consequent frayed tempers.

In hunting woodcock, one of our important game birds, clothing should be chosen with care. According to the guide book a man, to keep comfortable, should have some cotton or lightweight flannel shirts, three weights of woolen overshirts, lightweight wool underwear, waterproof footwear, army fatigue pants, a baseball cap, shooting glasses, light leather shooting gloves to protect the hands from scratches and cuts, and a shooting vest or belt to carry shells and birds. Are you beginning to see where all that money goes?

So much for equipment for upland bird shooting. What about shore birds like the curlew, the gallinule, the plover, the yellow-legs, and the snipe? Shore bird shooting has become pretty much a thing of the past, ever since they became so reduced in numbers by market shooters and sportsmen at the turn of the century. Decoys of the period are now kept in the Audubon Museum in Fairfield, Connecticut, where you can see reproductions of the turnstone, the knot, the willet, the dowitcher, and the sandpiper. The one shore bird that is still shot extensively is the rail. He has escaped the plunder of the commercial shooters principally because, after he has been picked and prepared, he doesn't usually offer more than a mouthful of food. In the animal world it pays off not to make too generous or tasty a dish.

Waterfowl offer the widest number of targets for the gunner. There are sixteen varieties of river and pond ducks, from baldplate to wood duck, and twenty-one kinds of bay and sea ducks, from bufflehead to scoter. There are also less important ducks like mergansers, ruddy ducks, masked ducks, and tree ducks. Of all the wild fowl on this continent, geese are the bird hunter's most highly prized game. Their wariness provides a challenge, and their flesh (unlike that of the rail) is very meaty and tastes delicious.

Different sections of the country offer different kinds of waterfowl hunting. The Maine coast is a good area for eiders (source of the old-fashioned eiderdown quilt) and scoters, known as "coots." In the Central Atlantic area of Long Island Sound, Great South Bay, and Barnegat Bay, the scoter also forms the largest part of the duck population, with some teal, mallards, and many black ducks. In the South, the Currituck and Pamlico Sound areas offer bird havens that attract hunters from thousands of miles away for canvasbacks, redheads, scaup, and Canadian geese. Currituck provides wild celery and other water plants that give the birds a good flavor, while at Pamlico the birds feed more on fish and mussels, with predictable results.

In the Midwest, the famous Bear River marshes of Utah offer more species (sixteen) of waterfowl in greater numbers than almost anywhere in the country. On the Pacific Coast the hunter can also find a greater variety in more abundance than on the East Coast, and Canada is another source of water birds, as any Eskimo will tell you. Texas and Louisiana are the spots for blue geese and snow geese.

In all waterfowl hunting, no matter where, the chief luring devices are the decoys, which are placed in the water so that the bird will think he sees some friends he can join for a bite and a nap, and will come down from his flight to investigate. After the decoys have been set out, the hunter hides behind a blind. The interesting point about a blind is that, like a girdle, it cannot always be both good *and* comfortable. Its purpose is to blind the duck to the presence of the hunter, his boat, or his dog. This utilitarian purpose must come before comfort and ease. The paradoxical part about this is that blinds that blend with the scenery are sometimes no more successful than blinds that, to us, seem to stick out in obvious contrast to their surroundings. A bird will be alarmed by a bright, flashing object in the blind, like a thermos or lunch box or an empty shell case glinting in the sun. It may also be warned off if the outline of a boat is left visible.

There are fixed blinds and floating blinds, reef blinds, sunken blinds, grass blinds, pit blinds, and stake blinds. None of them is very roomy or cozy, and a waterfowler must really be a devotee of the sport to sit in a cramped position, surrounded by dampness for hours on end. If you can't quite comprehend it, look at it this way. The sportsman undoubtedly can't understand why his wife will squeeze herself into a girdle that tortures her, in order to wear a dress that is a size too small. We all, male and female, are ready to make sacrifices and endure discomfort for a cause that is sufficiently important to us.

HUNTING THE SMALL ANIMALS

Small game hunting is fun for the hunter, and often requires less skill than big game hunting. Possum, a nocturnal animal, is hunted at night, with dogs which tree him for the sportsman. Prairie dogs are hunted in early morning or late afternoon, when they make the best targets, since they seem to take an early-afternoon siesta underground.

The cottontail rabbit is the number-one small game in North America. The main reason for this is that he is easily available in almost every one of the United States. He can be found in the suburbs, as well as out in the wilds. Another reason for his popularity is that the open season is a long one because of his abundance. No expensive equipment is required either. A gun, some shells, and a hunting license are all that is needed. However, the sport is said to be improved by the presence of a dog, usually a beagle, a basset, a dachshund, or a springer spaniel.

Most coon hunting, like possum hunting, is done at night, and dogs are specially trained to be coonhounds. Squirrels, in many sections of the country, run rabbits a close second as the favorite quarry. Woodchuck (a form of "varmint") hunting is chiefly a rifleman's sport, and several guns have been developed recently for that purpose alone.

AFTER BIGGER GAME

Although we usually associate the expression "big game hunting" with African safaris, there are actually quite a few big game species left on this continent, so your sportsman doesn't have to travel quite that far. There are pronghorn antelope in Wyoming; brown bear, black bear, grizzlies, and polar bear in Alaska; bison in South Dakota, Montana, and Canada; wild boar in Tennessee; caribou in Washington; elk in Oregon; Rocky Mountain goat in Montana and Washington; moose in Maine and Canada; peccary in Texas; mountain sheep in Colorado; and deer of some kind nearly everywhere.

Sportsman Francis E. Sell of Riverton, Oregon, calls deer "the most canny of all big game." * This fact, together with their prevalence, accounts for the popularity of deer hunting. Besides being canny, deer are speedy. Their top speed is around forty-five miles an hour, although they don't achieve this very often. A representative speed would be about seventeen to eighteen miles an hour, which only the fastest Olympic track star can approach.

---

* *The Deer Hunter's Guide*, Stackpole Books, 1964.

Because of this speed, the outdoorsman has only a matter of seconds in which to make his kill accurately. In order to make a humane killing, the sportsman must be not more than 100 to 120 yards away, and 50 yards is preferable. One reads reports of deer being shot at distances of 300 to 400 yards; but the hunter, like the fisherman, is likely to get fanciful when recounting the highlights of his experiences. If your sportsman is guilty of such lapses, there is no point in disputing it and spoiling his fun. Just don't let yourself be taken in.

The successful deer hunter must become quite a naturalist—learning deer habits, knowing the wind directions, and reading deer trails. At feeding time the deer is a gentleman, and it is always "ladies first" with him. Being aware of this, your sportsman has a good chance of getting his buck if he waits quietly until after the does have passed. The hunter hesitates to shoot a doe, even on the rare occasions when it is permissible because of deer overpopulation. Thus, with all those bucks being knocked off, there is a surplus of lonely females that is even worse than in the human population. This situation is solved among deer by each buck's having a harem of from five to fifteen does, a solution no longer accepted in our western human society.

A deer hunter must know the wind direction at every moment, so that he does not tip off the game to his presence by his scent. There will be spots where the wind drift is downslope in the morning, but the heat of the day will send it upward to where the hunter is waiting. Such spots produce successful hunting during the day only when it is overcast or a storm is approaching, so the hunter must change his position on clear days to be far enough away so that the air currents don't betray him. Your hunter must learn to understand these thermal winds, or air currents, set in motion by temperature changes. Sometimes these winds are so slight that they are almost imperceptible to a hunter. But the deer, which is so delicately attuned to nature, always travels with his nose into the wind. If the man has misjudged his location, the deer can detect his presence.

Deer like warmth, both for the pleasure of being warm and for the nutritious food found in warmer spots; so sunlit areas are more productive of deer than shady ones. They seek food and shelter in territories with a southern exposure. When your sportsman enters such an area and comes across tracks, he must know how to read them in order to plan his hunt. The larger tracks will usually mean a buck, the smaller ones a doe or fawn. Sometimes a large doe will make correspondingly large tracks; but she usually picks up her feet daintily, while the buck will leave a characteristic dragging of the hooves. There is no really accurate and dependable indication of deer sex from tracks, although some experienced outdoorsmen claim to know not only that a print has been made by a buck, but what size antlers he carries!

THE GUN

Deer, like most big game, are hunted mainly with a rifle. According to Larry Koller, author of *The Golden Guide to Guns* (Golden Press, 1961), "The distinguishing characteristic of the rifle is the series of shallow, spiral grooves cut into the inner surface of its barrel." These are the rifling from which the gun gets its name, and they give spin to the bullet as it is forced through the barrel, making for more accurate flight over a longer range. There are several kinds of rifle actions. Bolt-action is strong and heavy and requires enough manual activity to help steady the nervous sportsman. Lever-action is flat and compact, as it was once widely used for guns carried on horseback. Pump (or slide) action is lightweight and quick and easy to use. The autoloader can perhaps be fired faster by the hunter than any other rifle. It is therefore preferred by some outdoorsmen for fast-running game such as deer. It is best used by the calm, steady type of hunter, who won't be tempted to act like a movie gangster handling a sub-machine gun.

Small-bore rifles and shotguns are preferred for small game. Although autoloaders are the popular repeating models in this type of rifle, bolt-action models are preferable for some small game hunting and virtually all target shooting. The names of these rifles are old and familiar: the Winchester 69, Remington 511A, Marlin 80, Savage 5, and others. Slide and lever actions also make good choices for small game hunters. The current interest in the old West, spurred by TV shows, has encouraged the revival of some old designs used in that period, such as the Marlin 56 and Mossberg Palomino. Deer are best hunted with a lightweight, short-barreled rifle equipped with a good sight, like the Remington 760C carbine or one of the several suitable Winchesters. Different kinds of rifles are required for long-range shooting at quarries like mountain goats, for medium game like antelope, for the so-called "varmints" like woodchuck, coyote, or bobcat, and for big game in the timber country like moose, elk, and caribou.

The shotgun is probably the most widely used hunter's gun in the United States. It is good for birds, rabbits, and foxes, as well as bobcats and similar predators. The way it is usually employed, a shotgun throws a load of shot, rather than a single slug or bullet, in an even pattern at a reasonably short range—its usefulness falling off rapidly at ranges beyond thirty-five yards.

The revolver and the automatic, loosely referred to as handguns, are of limited use in hunting, as they are hard to shoot accurately and usually have a relatively limited effective range. They are also difficult to own because of restrictive legislation. (Naturally this makes every man want to own one.) The big-bore handgun, however, is widely used as a supplementary hunting weapon—often with a 'scope—in the West, where game is large and the hunter frequently works on horseback.

THE MAN BEHIND THE GUN

No matter what kind of gun he uses, it is the man behind the gun who matters. Garry Anderson, the Nebraska divinity student who took a gold medal in shooting at the Tokyo Olympics, has said that the mind must be in absolute control of all the muscle systems of the body in order for a man to achieve championship shooting ability. This is true in the field as well as on the rifle range, for it is there that the mental discipline acquired in practice is finally put to use. While mental effort cannot in itself be exhausting, the muscular tension involved in shooting accurately can be physically tiring. When your sportsman comes home from a day's shooting all tired out from carrying a gun weighing only a few pounds, you can now understand why.

THE HUNTING DOG

If the gun is the hunter's right hand, the dog is his left hand. A good hunting dog, being as affectionate and lovable as any other kind of dog, is the one part of the hunter's equipment of interest to the whole family. There are many hunting breeds, from the basset, the beagle, and the black and tan, to the various spaniels and retrievers. Then come the beautiful setters, the short-haired pointers, the plott hounds, the fox hounds, the weimaraner, and even the dachshund. Actually, almost any dog can be turned into a hunter and takes to it quite naturally, as you may have begun to suspect when you discovered the family terrier stalking a pigeon or bluejay.

With or without a dog, hunting is great sport; but it is even better with one, as anybody who has owned and loved a dog can understand.

8

Cues on the Camper

There are almost as many types of camping as there are varieties of hunters and fishermen. There are backpacking trips afoot for a day or a week. There are canoe trips and packhorse trips. For those who want their roughing it smoothed off a little around the edges, there are station wagon trips, trailer trips, and houseboat trips. Some people even consider staying in a cabin in the mountains "camping out," since it may involve cooking in the open and taking the risk of having the food supplies raided by a hungry bear or a porcupine after the salt.

Enjoying Life as a Sportsman's Wife

With the development of improved lightweight equipment and comfortable outdoor clothing styles for women, camping is often a family affair. Much of the literature available from the government, or from private groups like the Sierra Club, describes family camping outings as a popular thing. Even the sports magazines, with their predominantly male readership, provide information on family camping vacations. Most of these articles make camping sound so delightful that a casual female reader might be caught up in the writers' enthusiasm. But she would be disenchanted by a piece with a more frank title and outlook, like "How to Beat Bugs," by C. B. Colby in the December, 1962, issue of *Outdoor Life*. Another that might give her pause would be Bradford Angier's "Breads You Can Bake in Camp," in *National Wildlife* (February-March, 1964). These two articles point up the reasons why women think twice before joining in their sportsman's camping trips. The outdoors isn't all beautiful scenery, fresh air, and healthful exercise. It can be mosquitoes, black flies, deer and moose flies, midges, chiggers, ticks, spiders, and centipedes. And that's only the biters! The stingers include wasps, hornets, bees, and sometimes even scorpions. In addition, camping isn't all nature study, hunting, or fishing. It's cooking! As if a woman didn't get enough of that at home.

Whether you plan to leave the camping in the family strictly up to the males or want to find out its hazards and pleasures so that you know what to expect on a joint excursion, it is a nice wifely gesture to discover what this camping business is all about, so you can show some interest in the expeditions.

BACKPACKING, THE HEARTY APPROACH

The simplest trip is the daily pack trip, with a light rucksack to carry everything the hunter needs for his convenience, from lunch to waterproof matchbox to maps. For longer jaunts, the knapsack camper must be a pretty hardy individual. His rewards will be proportionate. He will have better hunting and fishing than the man who travels by car, because he will be able to reach more inaccessible, less widely hunted areas. Backpacking for long distances should be done in company with a friend, because no matter how experienced your sportsman may be, he can run into a situation where he needs someone else's help. The friend should be one with whose character he is completely familiar, for extended companionship under rough conditions can reveal unsuspected incompatibilities.

In backpacking the most important items are food, shelter (a small tent or fly), and bedding; they account for most of the approximately twenty-five pounds of equipment that the sportsman will probably be carrying. The concentrated foods now available—especially the new freeze-dried products—combined with occasional meals of game or fish, can keep him going for maybe a month or so. If your outdoorsman is new at the backpacking game, he ought to get himself in trim first with a few rehearsals, and keep his trips short to start with, so that he can use a lighter amount of food. His feet and legs should be toughened up and his boots broken in. He should also discard all but absolute essentials of equipment, to keep his pack load down to a weight convenient for him to carry long distances. It has been suggested by experts that a fork can always be cut from a tree, a hunting knife can double as table knife, and a frying pan makes an adequate plate. Two light aluminum pots will take care of heating food and drink. They weigh little and can be packed with food to conserve space. The foods will be chiefly cereals, sugar, salt, bacon, and dehydrated high-protein products.

See that your sportsman carries along plenty of socks and a pair of tennis shoes or moccasins, in addition to his hiking boots, so that he can wash his feet at night or at lunch stops and get into dry socks and soft shoes to rest them. Band Aids and adhesive tape should be supplied to protect sore spots.

In backpacking, after the feet are assured of comfort, the next most important thing is a good night's sleep. The shelter may be anything from a pocket-sized sheet of plastic to a three-and-a-half-pound tent made of plastic, nylon, or balloon silk. Canvas is too heavy to carry around on the back. Sleeping bags come filled with eiderdown, feathers, wool, kapok, dacron, polyester, or celacloud acetate. They can run in price from eight to a hundred dollars; a good inexpensive feather bag can be purchased in a military surplus store. There are lightweight plastic air mattresses for a few dollars that add to sleeping comfort.

After rest, the third necessity is some refueling of the human machine. On trails where fuel wood is available, cooking the food will be no problem, as long as matches have been brought along or the outdoorsman knows how to start a fire. There are certain stretches on some trails, like the John Muir in California, that are barren and rocky and have little wood for fuel. For such situations it is a good idea to carry a small knapsack stove, a little over a

pound in weight, that will hold a pint of gas, naphtha, or
benzine, for boiling water. A backpacker should of course
have his fire permit, as well as a map and a compass.

In fact, a thoughtful wife will see that her sportsman
makes up a complete list of everything he can possibly
need on his trip, and will then check it off as he fills his
knapsack to see that he doesn't forget anything. * It isn't
like packing for any other kind of trip—where a slip-up
doesn't really matter, since he will be staying in a hotel
with a drugstore and room service. There is no room
service where he's going. If your husband complains that
his pack is heavy, remind him that he will be eating up
much of the weight, and his pack should be two pounds
lighter every day.

THE SADDLE-AND-PACK METHOD

An outdoorsman who finds backpacking a strain can always go on what is known as a "hiking-pack" trip, where
a packhorse, mule, or burro may be used to carry the
heavy pack. A mule or horse can be rented for this purpose
for around $6.00 a day. A burro costs as little as $3.00 a
day and can carry from fifty to seventy-five pounds. A
more expensive way to get to the desired spot, but one that
saves wear and tear on legs and feet, is the saddle-and-pack
method.

If you happen to own a stable of horses, then you can
saddle some for riding, pack others for hauling, and send

---

* A new book, HOME IN YOUR PACK, by Bradford Angier
(Stackpole Books), gives the story on what he'll need and how to
pack it. In this book there is much of interest to the distaff side of
the camping family.

your husband on his way with his own saddle-and-pack outfit. If you don't belong to the horsey set, then your sportsman will have to hire a licensed packer with a permit to operate in the spot he has chosen for his camping expedition. He can have the packer bring him to his chosen hunting or fishing location, and then pick him up a week or two later to bring him out. Or he may prefer to keep the saddle-and-pack stock with him, so that he can move around from one site to another at will. Sometimes the packer supplies everything needed for camping out, such as cook, guide, wrangler, food, and camping equipment— and the cost is naturally commensurate, about $25.00 per person per day. A sportsman who supplies his own equipment will only have to pay the $6.00 per animal a day, plus another $15.00 a day for the packer, plus the packer's food and equipment. When there are several hunters or fishermen together, the cost per person can be minimized. If your sportsman is no horseman, he can get a stripped-down motor scooter called a "Tote Goat" for wilderness use.

ROUGHING IT BY AUTOMOBILE

Motor camping has become very popular in the last decade, with the number of camp sites tripling in that period. These are the places to go for modern conveniences and sanitary facilities. For those who feel that they are not really camping out unless they provide their own shelter, build their own fireplaces, and dig their own waste-disposal units, there are still plenty of wilderness camps. To make it easier, the outdoorsman can drive to the nearest point and then hike or pack in to camp.

For tenting—whatever the camp site—there are any number of models from which to choose. There is a little two-man tent called the "Himalayan," for high altitudes. There is the umbrella tent, a larger tent with a portico. For a simple shelter, a polyethylene cloth or tarpaulin can be dropped across a rope stretched between two trees, and the four corners staked to the ground. There is the Mt. Logan high-altitude, three-man tent with a zippered air vent at top and sod cloth underneath. There is the big wall tent, which can be supported by stripped saplings for security. If your husband is experienced with tents, great! If not, it would be a wise precaution for him to practice erecting one in the back yard before going on his trip, as the directions are pretty complicated and each type of tent has its own particular erection tricks, from the explorer tent to the army tent to the lean-to tent, or pup tent.

If tent-erecting raises your sportsman's blood pressure, he might be better off in one of the self-contained or partly self-contained mobile outfits. The modern station wagon makes a versatile camp wagon. A custom foam rubber mattress can be made for it, covering the rear from the back of the front seat to the closed tailgate. The opened tailgate can be used for both work space and dining table. Newspaper can be taped over the windows for privacy, in case of a peeping tomtit or a voyeurist woodpecker. Mesh can be taped over windows to keep out insects. A lamp can be plugged into the cigarette-lighter socket, and there he is! All set to read his favorite Ian Fleming novel in bed.

The bus-type car like the Volkswagen "Microbus" and

the Chevrolet "Greenbriar," or the Ford "Falcon" with a bus-type body, provides a fine camping outfit. Dodge now also offers such a model. A sportsman can sleep in it, cook, dress, and keep gear in it as well. When not in use for camping, it makes a practical car to bus the children around in and to pile bulky shopping in.

Another self-contained camping outfit consists of a house-trailer coach body adjusted to fit on the back of a pickup truck, like Chevrolet's "Fleetside" pickup. Ford also offers several such body options, in their "Falcon" and regular lines. A large pickup truck with a travel-coach body offers first-class travel facilities. In fact it can look so appealing that sportsmen who want to use one of them exclusively for fishing or hunting may find that their wives are eyeing their departure with a suspicious glint of envy. If you should be one of these wives, don't worry. According to an authority, although the coach body *can* be removed and stored between trips, this usually proves such a chore that they are left attached permanently. The owners then take their families out on frequent week end outings to justify their own lack of energy.

The separate small trailer known as a travel trailer is comfortable and convenient, but expensive. A thirteen-foot one would be easy to pull and will sleep three people. The larger house trailers, or mobile homes, such as the 55-footer, require a truck to pull them. For a trailer to be truly mobile, it must not hold up traffic or take up too much space in the camp ground, so the smaller sized travel trailers—usually less than twenty-two feet long—are preferable. A good, light, inexpensive trailer is the trailer tent, which they say can be erected in a few minutes.

These compact, folding, tent-trailer outfits carry all the camp equipment, so the car is left free for extra luggage, or for carrying a boat.

INDIAN FASHION, IN A CANOE

If your husband is a real boatman, he will always prefer to travel by the canoe-and-portage method. There is a vast area in North America, with a plentiful supply of game and fish, that can be reached in no other way. Maine, Wisconsin, and Minnesota are famous for their canoeing waters, and the long rivers of the South are also navigable by canoe. Canada has a network of lakes and rivers in the moose, caribou, deer, bear, grouse, and fishing country. Because a canoe is light, it can easily be portaged around dangerous rapids and falls, and in between waterways, on one man's shoulders. Since it moves quietly, it can be paddled soundlessly toward game. Because it can be maneuvered with its occupants facing front, it can be used successfully in fairly rapidly running waters. The canoe is one of our most useful inheritances from the Indian.

Modern canoes are no longer made of birchbark; but the closer they approach the original Indian design, the better they function. Some of the finest are constructed of canvas stretched over a light wooden shell. Excellent newer models are those made of aluminum or fiberglass, with air chambers for floatability. There are collapsible canoes with light metal or wood frames which are convenient, but they aren't so roomy or seaworthy as the rigid models. The light, pleasure canoe adapted for romance in quiet waters, is not always ideal for wilderness use. So-called "guide" canoes are better for navigating in large lakes and rapid water, and the "prospector" type is considered tops. These are usually at least 17 feet long, 37 inches wide, and 14 inches deep, with a flattish bottom.

Canoes are now also being equipped with light outboard motors, to get the sportsman there and back faster and with less physical effort. Unfortunately, the sound of the motor tends to drive game away, and sitting in a canoe in an immobile position can give a man a charley horse.

Motor or no motor, the problems of canoeing come at the portage spots, where first the (let us assume) two men carry their backpacks across the land to the next embarkation point. Then they return to the canoe. One of them will carry the bed roll and any remaining paraphernalia, and the other the canoe. If your husband is one of these two hypothetical men, he will have to take his turn at carrying the canoe now and then. A twelve-foot canoe weighs around forty pounds, an eighteen-footer about eighty pounds or more. Imagine him with this weight balanced on his head, back, and shoulders as he attempts to walk over uneven terrain with a restricted view of the trail ahead!

Game can be sighted and stalked in a canoe, as it was done by the Indians. Sometimes the game can be shot right from the canoe by the bow man, while at others it will be necessary to land and make the stalk through nearby woods. At best, a canoe is an unsteady base from which to shoot, so it pays for the hunter to step ashore for his shot if he wants to avoid winging a squirrel when aiming at a moose.

A more elaborate type of camping cruise was described in the May, 1964, issue of *Outdoor Life*, in an article by

Bruce McPherson. After months of planning, he and seven friends started out in two fully loaded station wagons, trailering two powerboats—a 21-foot aluminum cabin cruiser and an 18-foot aluminum runabout—plus a 15-foot canoe. They drove all night, the five hundred miles from the Grand Rapids, Michigan, area up to the Canadian side of Lake Superior, in order to fish some famous rainbow trout streams. They spent a week looking for a stream that would produce enough trout for all, and finally found the spot in the University River—where they fished their limits of five apiece. Unless you sometimes fish, too, you'll probably find it difficult to understand why anyone would go to all that trouble to catch a few trout. Maybe they did it for the same reason men claim they climb mountains, "Just because they are there!"

PLACES TO GO

While Canada has a great deal of undeveloped land and water where the hunter and fisherman can enjoy themselves, the United States also has vast national parks, national forests, and wilderness areas where the outdoorsman and his family can find suitable recreation. There are thirty-one national parks with roads, trails, and camp sites constructed by the National Park Service, plus hotels, lodges, cabins, and bus transportation provided by private concessionaires. The purpose of the national *parks* is to preserve nature for the appreciation of the visitor. There are also 154 national *forests*, established by presidential proclamation. Here nature is not only preserved but is also put to use, by having its water supplies safeguarded, its timber resources controlled, and its forest ranges managed for livestock grazing. A favorable habitat for wildlife is also maintained, and one-third of the country's big game animals make their homes there. National forests provide opportunities for camping, picknicking, hiking, hunting, and fishing. Regular camp and picnic areas are equipped with fireplaces and grates, tables, sanitary facilities, and safe drinking water. The Forest Service also maintains more primitive sections, known as *wilderness areas*.

It is the hiker or backpacker who really sees most of the wild country still left in the United States. He has his choice of trails with picturesque names like The Pacific Crest Trail, The Oregon Skyline Trail, The Sierra Crest Trail, and The Appalachian Trail. Their descriptions are as fascinating as the travel section of your Sunday newspaper. It makes you want to get right out there with your pack on your back, when you read of the Tehachapis, the Mojave desert, the Sierra Nevada, the Olympic mountains, Glacier Peak, Goat Rocks, Tahoe-Yosemite and Yuba Gap, Sequoia-Kings Canyon, Franconia, the Kittatinny Range, the Blue Ridge mountains, and Harper's Ferry. Naturally once you've reflected on the wear and tear on your feet, and the strain on your leg and back muscles, you will probably let your sportsman hit the trail, while you go back to dreaming about a Caribbean cruise.

THINGS TO TAKE

When your husband is out in the woods and you are at home, you won't be too preoccupied to give him an occasional thought. You may wonder what he and his friends are up to, how they are enjoying themselves, and most important, whether they are safe. The best way to avoid wasted time worrying over your outdoorsman is to see that he leaves the house fully equipped with every device to protect his health and welfare that it is possible to carry along.

In the first place, make sure that he remembers his compass, that handy little gadget that helps a man to find his way around at sea, in the wilderness, or even in the middle of a strange city. The cheap compass with a pointer needle over a paper marker is not recommended, as it breaks easily, the markings are inadequate, and the needle swings wildly when the compass is moved or placed near metal. A more expensive compass has a stabilized needle, and luminescent markings that can be read in the dark. Top-grade compasses use liquids in which the needle appears to float.

Along with the compass, the outdoorsman will want some reliable maps. There are the automobile-club maps, with which you no doubt are familiar, and small trail maps issued by the Forest and National Park Service. For the sportsman going into the back woods, however, the most serviceable map is the Geological Survey topographic map. These cost around a dollar and can be purchased at most modern stationery stores, at Forest and National Park Service headquarters, or directly from the Superintendent of Documents, Washington, D.C. 20402. Smaller quadrangle maps of the particular area through which the hunter or fisherman will travel cost forty to fifty cents apiece. A flashlight is another indispensable item on the check list for night safety. Sunburn lotion is advisable as a daytime safety measure. Sharp-edged instruments should have leather or canvas guards.

A first aid kit is a must. There are helpful first aid cards and pamphlets put out by the government and the Metropolitan Life Insurance Company. The former is called *First Aid*, L-12, and is for sale by the Superintendent of Documents, Washington, D.C. 20402, for five cents. The second is *First Aid for the Family*, obtainable free from the Metropolitan Life Insurance Company, 1 Madison Avenue, New York, N.Y. 10010.

The Government Printing Office in Washington also puts out many booklets on camping and its enjoyment:

Camping	20¢
National Forest Vacations	30¢
Backpacking in the National Forest Wilderness	15¢
Camping Facilities in Areas Administered by the National Park Service	10¢
Wilderness	20¢
Reclamation's Recreational Opportunities	15¢
Areas Administered by the National Park Service	20¢
The Appalachian Trail	5¢
The National Park System (two maps)	
Eastern U.S.	20¢
Western U.S.	20¢

These are all available from the Superintendent of Documents, Washington, D.C. 20402.

9

How to Handle Game for Gourmets

Would you know what to do if your sportsman brought home a buffalo or an elephant? There's nothing to it! Open the Farmers' Almanack for 1964 to the month of July, and there you will find a recipe for elephant stew. "Cut the elephant into small bite-size pieces," they say. "This should take about two months. Add enough brown gravy to cover. Cook over kerosene fire for about four weeks at 465 degrees. This will serve thirty-eight hundred people."

Does that frighten you? Be reassured. Not many men

go hunting for elephant. As for buffalo, the Wise Encyclopedia of Cookery (Wise and Company, 1948) tells us convincingly, "The cooking of a cut of buffalo need hold no terrors for the homemaker fortunate enough to receive it." It is the game most similar to beef, they explain, and can be roasted, potroasted, or broiled.

Game should be no more of a cooking problem than any domestic fish, flesh, or fowl—especially today, when it can be taken to a butcher at a processing plant to be hung (when necessary), then cut and wrapped for deep-freezing, and used as required. And few things give a more "special occasion" atmosphere than serving venison, partridge, or rainbow trout to guests accustomed to ordinary fare like beef, chicken, and shrimp. You can acquire a reputation for gourmet cooking with very little effort on your part, since it is the main ingredient—the game—that makes the dish unusual. Most ordinary cookbooks do not devote many pages to game cookery; so it is suggested, if you want to get the best results, that you consult a game cookbook, or one with a large game section, like *Great Dishes of the World* (Random House, 1964), by Robert Carrier.

A game meal is exceptionally high in protein. Hare, grouse, partridge, and pheasant in fact have even more protein than most meats. As for fish, you know how that is reputed to reduce the fat content of the diet.

GETTING THE BEST FLAVOR WITH FISH

Since fish is the simplest food to cook, let's begin with some suggestions on its preparation. Some fish can be cooked in any number of different ways, while others taste best when prepared by one or two particular methods. Walleye can be fried in deep fat, sauteed, poached, baked, or broiled with equally good results, while whitefish or shad are preferably broiled planked or baked.

Oily fishes are usually best broiled or baked. This group includes herring, pompano, smelt, trout, salmon, and mackerel. Herring, pompano, trout, and salmon steaks may also be sauteed in butter or poached. Lake or brook trout is especially good when boiled au bleu.

Boiled Brook Trout au Bleu

Two brook trout, 2 lb. each	Lemon
Court-bouillon *(see below)*	Hollandaise sauce *(see be-*
Parsley	*low)*

Wipe the trout, then plunge quickly into boiling court-bouillon (see below). Simmer gently 15 to 20 minutes. Arrange on a hot platter, decorated with parsley and lemon quarters. Serve with hollandaise sauce.

Court-Bouillon

2 qt. water	Pinch of thyme
2/3 cup vinegar	2 bay leaves
2 tbsp. salt	Tsp. dried parsley
2 small carrots, sliced	12 peppercorns
2 small onions, sliced	Bring to boil and add fish

Hollandaise Sauce

½ cup butter	2 tbsp. hot water
2 egg yolks	Salt and pepper
1 tbsp. lemon juice	

For the hollandaise sauce, separate the butter into two portions, placing one of them in upper part of double boiler. Add egg yolks and lemon juice, place over hot *(not boiling)* water and stir constantly until butter melts. Add remaining butter and continue stirring. Add hot water and cook, still stirring, until thick. Remove from heat and season.

With all that fancy trimming, I suppose anything would taste good; but beside tasting good, trout has vitamins A and B and a 445-calory value per pound. If that hollandaise sauce, added to the fish's own caloric value, sounds a bit rich, you can always stick to simple broiling. Trout should be split and preferably boned, leaving the skin unbroken, and broiled over glowing coals or under a good electric broiling unit.

The white-fleshed, rather dry fish, include black bass, crappies, sunfishes, white and yellow bass, and yellow perch, in the fresh water species. In the same class are such marine fish as flounders, soles, sea bass, weakfish, croakers, drums, cods, swordfish, etc. These fish can be baked with wines and sauces or bacon strips, fried in deep fat, oven-poached in milk or au gratin, sauteed, and even grilled. Any of these fish may be served a la meuniere, which means with a melted and browned butter sauce containing a few drops of lemon juice and some chopped parsley.

Grunts, snappers, porgies, groupers, and whitings are excellent prepared creole style, in gumbo, or chowder. Muskellunge, northern pike, and pickerels are rather too bony for some tastes, and catfish have a strong flavor which does not appeal to all palates. Those who like them prepare the pikes by baking or frying, and the catfish lovers dip them in milk and corn meal and deep-fry them in hot fat.

SERVING WILD FOWL

So much for fish. Now let us see what can be done with the fowl family. You don't need to learn a separate recipe for each bird unless you wish, as most recipes can be used for more than one. The recipe for Dove Purlough (also known as Pilaf or Purleau), for instance, can also be used for quail, woodcock, pigeons, or rail.

Dove Purlough

After a dozen or so birds have been plucked or skinned and drawn, saving the hearts and livers, put the following ingredients into a heavy two-gallon pot with birds, hearts, and livers. Cover. Simmer slowly for three hours.

2 qts. of stock (or 8 bouillon cubes and water)	6 peeled and diced tomatoes
½ pound butter (or margarine)	Large pinch marjoram
	1 tsp. pepper
6 medium onions, diced	1 tsp. chili powder
1 cup chopped parsley	3 tbsp. salt
	2½ cups rice

Stuffed Roast Pheasant

After a pheasant has been hung at least a week, and the feathers plucked (by the hunter, we hope), it can be cooked in any one of a number of fascinating-sounding ways: a la Bohemienne, en Cocotte, a la Creme, with Oranges and Chestnuts, and Paprika. A simple and good way is old-fashioned roasted and stuffed.

1 pheasant	1 wineglass sherry
2 oz. butter	1 tbsp. red currant jelly
2 strips bacon	Juice of ½ lemon

Stuffing

½ lb. sausage meat	Dried parsley
1 apple	Salt and pepper
1 egg	

Mix stuffing ingredients and stuff the bird. Wrap the bacon around it, dot it with butter, and roast in a moderate oven (350°) for 45 minutes. Drain off surplus fat and pour wine over the bird, adding jelly, lemon juice, salt, and pepper. Cook another 15 minutes, basting twice with the gravy.

Quails with Endive

After four quails have been plucked, drawn, and cut in half, use them in the following recipe:

4 quails	8 heads endive
1 slice ham	8 strips lean bacon
½ pt. water and chicken bouillon cube	1 oz. butter

Wrap each half-bird in a strip of bacon. Blanch endives in boiling water for a few minutes, then arrange them in a large casserole on the slice of ham. Dot with butter and place birds on top. Pour in stock and seasoning, cover tightly, and cook in moderate oven (350°) for about an hour.

Smothered Grouse

Cut into serving pieces. Roll in seasoned flour. In large frying pan, brown pieces slowly on both sides in ½ cup hot fat. Pour 1 cup of milk or light cream into pan.

Cover and cook over low heat until tender, or about one hour. If you prefer, you can cook the liver, hearts and gizzards in a cup of water with salt, pepper, and a pinch of celery salt for 20 minutes. Pour this over the birds, which have been placed in a casserole, together with a few teaspoons of onion flakes and some diced carrots, adding enough sour cream to cover. Cook for an hour in medium oven (325-350°).

Wild Duck

Wild duck, I've been told, should merely be allowed to fly through the oven. It can be stuffed with cooked wild rice, raw diced apple, prunes, or orange. Really rare duck is roasted in a very hot oven (500°) for 20 minutes or slightly longer, and basted frequently with wine, melted butter or margarine. If your family or guests do not like rare meat, then let the bird remain in a hot oven (450°) for 45 minutes to an hour, basting with a mixture of melted butter and Burgundy wine. Rare roast duck is like rare meat of any kind, mouth-watering to some but alarming to others, depending on their tastes. If you like, you can slice your duck, place the slices in a skillet, cover with duck gravy, and simmer for 2 or 3 minutes before serving.

Duck Gravy

Simmer liver, heart, and skinned gizzard in a cup of water, along with a little celery and onion. When tender, remove and dice and return to water. Then add a cup of sauce made by mixing a bouillon cube and two teaspoons of cornstarch with a cup of cold water, and bring to a boil.

RABBIT AND RACCOON RECIPES

There are many recipes for rabbit, the most popular of small game. He can be barbecued or curried, or jugged, or made into the famous old German dish, hasenpfeffer, after he has been skinned, cleaned, and cut into portions.

Hasenpfeffer

1 rabbit	3 bay leaves
Vinegar	Salt and pepper
Water	3 tbsp. cooking oil
Onion flakes	1 cup sour cream
Handful of whole cloves	Toasted bread triangles

Place rabbit portions in bowl and cover with equal parts of water and vinegar. Add a tablespoon of onion flakes, the bay leaves and cloves, salt and pepper. Marinate for two days, keeping meat covered with liquid and turning frequently. Remove meat, pat dry with paper towels, then sear on all sides in hot fat. Drain off fat and add enough of the marinade to cover the meat once more. Cover pot and simmer until tender, about a half-hour. Before serving, remove bay leaves, add sour cream, bring to a rapid boil and serve on a hot platter, surrounded by toast triangles. Serve with stewed prunes, apricots, or other tart fruit.

Roast Stuffed Raccoon

A raccoon makes a good food, tasting a little like chicken or lamb. In preparing it for cooking, the fat is removed, and the raccoon is often parboiled, then transferred to an oven and roasted slowly. A young animal makes the best roast; the older one should be relegated to the stew pot.

4 or 5 lb. raccoon
Dash of pepper
4 oz. seedless raisins
2 sliced apples
2 tsp. salt

1 lb. mashed sweet potatoes
8 oz. breadcrumbs
2 oz. melted butter or margarine

Mix potatoes, raisins, breadcrumbs, apples, and melted butter, seasoning with salt and pepper. Wash meat thoroughly, then dry. Salt the inside and stuff with sweet potato mixture. Skewer and lace with string. Place in roasting pan and put in a moderate oven (325-350°) for 45 minutes a pound. When it is partially cooked, turn it so that all sides will brown.

DELICIOUS OPPORTUNITIES WITH VENISON

Most game is marinated before cooking, but remember that the longer you marinate, the stronger the "gamey" flavor. Twenty-four hours is sufficient, unless you desire a gamey meal. If the hide has been left on for any length of time, this also increases the gamey taste of the meat. The sooner after the kill the game can be skinned and taken to the butcher's cooling room to hang, the better. As far as preparation goes, deer, moose, elk, and bear can all be treated similarly. The neck can be used for stews, the legs can be roasted. The ribs make good chops, the short ribs can be roasted with tomato sauce. The flank makes a good stew. The loin, fillet, flank, and rump are fine for steaks. The saddle can be roasted or broiled.

Broiled Venison

Venison steak should be cooked like beef. It is best broiled to medium rare, as overcooking toughens it. If you can

cook it over charcoal, so much the better. If not, there
is a hickory-smoked salt sold in most luxury grocery
stores which will give it that outdoor flavor. The meat
should be an inch and a half thick at least, and should
be rubbed with a little oil and quickly seared on both
sides. Then reduce heat or place meat farther from the
fire and cook 8 minutes or so. It is safest to test for
doneness with a sharp knife until you have learned the
exact time that should be allowed.

Civet of Deer

8 lbs. deer meat (shoulder, neck, breast, and flank)
½ lb. deer liver
½ lb. salt pork

Marinade

4 tbsp. brandy
4 tbsp. olive oil
2½ glasses red wine
4 sprigs parsley
4 tops green celery
2 bay leaves
2 garlic cloves

½ tsp. thyme
1 tbsp. flour
2 doz. small white onions, sliced
2 doz. small mushrooms, peeled and sliced
Salt, pepper

Cut the meat into serving portions and place in a bowl.
Cover with the marinade and let stand for 6 hours. Par-
boil salt pork and cut into small cubes, then fry and
drain when brown. Add deer, drained and dried, and sear
on all sides. Moisten with marinade, cover, and bake in
moderate oven (350°) 40 minutes. Add a mixture of a
teaspoon of cornstarch and ½ cup cold water to the
gravy in pan. Heat, stirring constantly. When ready to
serve, add the deer liver, cubed small.

Roast Venison
(leg, shoulder, saddle, round)

Rub meat with clove of garlic and insert half a dozen slivers in fatty portions. Rub thoroughly with vegetable oil, and salt and pepper lightly. Dust with flour. Put in open roasting pan on rack, adding 1 cup of water to bottom of pan. Place in hot oven (450°) for 15 minutes to sear meat. Reduce heat to 350° and baste often with a spoon. Allow 12 minutes a pound for a rare roast, 14 minutes for medium. If you don't care to baste so frequently, lay thin strips of salt pork or bacon over the top of the roast, fastening them with toothpicks.

Basting Sauce

2/3 cup olive or vegetable oil	½ tsp. hot pepper sauce
	1/3 cup lemon juice
½ grated onion	½ tsp. salt
2 tbsp. ketchup	½ tsp. prepared mustard

Venison Steaks, German Style

2 lbs. thick venison steaks	1 tsp. brown sugar
2 carrots	1 head celery
1 onion	3 or 4 mushrooms
1 pint white wine	3 oz. butter
1 bouillon cube or 1 tsp. MBT	1 tbsp. cornstarch

Marinade the steaks overnight. Melt 1 oz. of butter or margarine and fry onion until it is brown. Add vegetables, and a pint of boiling water. Add MBT or bouillon cube and allow to simmer an hour. Thicken with cornstarch, mixed with a little cold water. Add the wine and sugar, and season. Strain the liquid and dip the steaks into the sauce. Melt the rest of the butter and fry the steaks on both sides quickly, until done medium rare. Add the sliced mushrooms. Serve with toast points and red currant jelly.

There are any number of other venison recipes: **Venison en Daube, Galantine of Venison, Venison en Papillote, Venison Saucisses Creole, Venison Cacciatore, Venison Marsala, and Venison Barbecue.** Venison liver is said to be the equal, if not the superior, of calves' liver when it comes from a young deer.

WHATEVER IT IS, YOU CAN COOK IT

If your sportsman brings home something more exotic than venison, you can still find a recipe for that if you consult a comprehensive game cookbook. Should he catch a whale some day at sea, whale meat makes delicious steaks and fine stew. If he visits Mexico or Panama, he may bring you home an iguana sometime. Never fear. The meat is white and tender, and good with a port or Madeira wine sauce. Does he hunt in alligator country? Steaks cut from the tail are reputed to be a delicacy. Is he likely to pick up a turtle in the Bahamas? Turtle fins can be grilled in butter with superb results.

Perhaps the best recipe of all for the wife of an outdoorsman is called "How to Cook a Husband," from a 1700 cookbook, of which the following is a small excerpt:

"Some women keep them in a stew by irritating ways and words. Others roast them. Some keep them in a pickle all their lives. It cannot be supposed that any husband will be tender and good managed in this way, but they are really delicious when properly treated. . . . Make a clear steady fire of love, neatness, and cheerfulness. Set him as near this as seems to agree with him. If he sputters and fizzes, do not be anxious; some husbands do this until quite done. Add a little sugar in the form of what the confectioners call kisses, but no vinegar or pepper on any account. A little spice improves them, but it must be used with judgment." *

* *Farmers' Almanack* (Almanac Publishing Company, 1964).

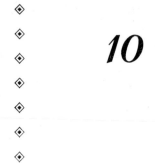

10

Speaking the Language of the Fisherman

This chapter contains a glossary of basic fishing terms, so that you can familiarize yourself with them and act knowing when your husband starts talking about a nylon filament leader or an oval-elipse spoon. In these few pages, the entire fishing vocabulary cannot be covered completely. If consequently you find yourself becoming confused in the middle of a conversation about a Welshman, when you know your sportsman's fishing companions are both Scandinavians, you can take one of two courses: (1) Inquire adoringly, while batting your eyes, "But darling, who or what is a Welshman?" (2) Keep your lips sealed and pretend to understand, consulting a dictionary later to discover that a Welshman is a smallmouth black bass.

Airboat. A light boat propelled by an aircraft propeller, for use in marshes and shallow lakes. Also, inflatable boats useful for backpacking trips.

Albacore. Large game fish, 15 to 30 pounds average size, found in Pacific waters, with record catches made off Catalina, California.

Amberjack. Atlantic game fish, abundant off Florida but found from Cape Cod to Brazil. Average size 10 to 15 pounds; but a catch of a 146-pound amberjack was once reported from Bermuda, and catches of over 70 pounds have been made off Bimini. If you'd like a trip to Bermuda or the Bahamas, you might remind your husband of this.

Anti-Backlash. Device to put tension on the reel spool to prevent overrun on the outgoing lure. Device to allow spool to run entirely free until the line slackens.

Automatic Reel. A reel with a spring facility to take up the line as it is brought in. As line is stripped out, it winds up springs within the reel. Tension thus supplied draws line back on reel spool when the force is released by a finger trigger.

Backlash. A backlash means the reel turns faster than the outgoing plug or lure is dragging the line through the guides, with resulting tangle, and temper, temper, temper!

Bait Casting. Technique of holding rod and guiding it with wrist and forearm so that thumb touches and controls reel spool; bait lands at desired spot (theoretically).

Bait Fishing. Fishing with worms, crayfish, crickets,

shrimp, frogs, minnows, and other live bait, or cut-up pieces of fish, rather than with artificial lures like plugs, spoons, and flies.

Ballou Special. A streamer fly.

Bamboo Rods. Rods of natural bamboo cane, still popular though hard to get because they come mainly from China.

Barracuda. Large game fish, found on both Atlantic and Pacific coasts, which is swift and sharp-toothed. Its foods are fishes, squid, and careless bathers.

Bass. Bass of one kind or another are found in almost every state in the country, in fresh water and salt.

Bass Bugs. Lures that have more body than flies but are made of the same materials: hair, wool, silk, etc. Popular in bass fishing.

Big Eye Jack. Member of Crevalle family found off Hawaii and Panama. Surely you remember the Crevalles?

Blades. Wobbler blades and spinners, used in construction of spoon. (*see* spoons)

Bluefish. Small game fish, average size 3 to 6 pounds, found in spring off Hatteras, North Carolina, New Jersey, and Long Island, and in Massachusetts in the summer.

Bluegill. Small member of sunfish family weighing less than a pound, popular and prevalent in the U.S. and southern Canada.

Bob-House. Glorified outhouse used for ice-fishing shelter.

Bocaccio. A kind of rockfish native to Southern California. Also the author of a book of naughty tales.

Bonefish. Spindle-shaped fish with piglike snout, 2 to 5 pounds.

Bonito. Open-water marine fish, taken by trolling.

Bream. Also called pinfish. Member of porgy family.

Buffalo. Fresh-water fish found in Arkansas, Kentucky, Louisiana, Minnesota, and Mississippi.

Bullhead. Popular fresh-water pan fish.

Candlefish. Pacific game fish, also known as sablefish and greenling.

Carp. A toothless fish, with grinders in its throat, found in rivers, streams, and lakes having mud bottoms.

Catalpa Worms. Small bait worms found in catalpa trees. Ecchh!

Catfish. A whiskery fish family with 1,000 odd species, one of which may inhabit your home aquarium.

Cero. Fish similar to Spanish mackerel caught off Florida Keys.

Chiro. Also known as big-eyed herring and as ladyfish. Plentiful in South Florida's inland salt water.

Chumming. Dropping loose bait overboard to attract fish.

Cobia. An Atlantic fish found in Chesapeake Bay from May to late summer, and in large numbers off Mississippi.

Corbina. A California member of the croaker family, and fine for surf casting.

Crappie. Comes in both black and white varieties, found nearly everywhere in lakes, streams, and rivers. One-half to one pound.

Creel. Basket for fish, of woven willow or canvas.

Croaker. Fish that makes a croaking noise with air bladder.

Cubera. Also known as red snapper. Range from Brazil to Florida, average weight 30 to 60 pounds.

Dark-House. Shelter for ice fishing, used in shallow water.

Dart Cast. A method of casting for use on small streams with overhanging brush.

Dolphin. A brilliantly colored fish found in Gulf Stream waters, averaging under 25 pounds. Not to be confused with the mammalian dolphin similar to the porpoise, which has been trained to perform in aquariums and is reputed to be as smart as we are, if not more so.

Drum. Same as croaker.

Dry Fly. Fly lure used to float on surface of the water.

Eagle Claw. Hook with point slightly turned in, so line of penetration and line of pull are identical.

Eel-Bob Lure. A pickled eel or eelskin, used for catching bass.

False Cast. Practice cast to get line out and dry a fly, or to give better control over direction and distance for actual cast.

Fathometer. Device for measuring depth of water from fishing boats.

Fingerlings. Young fish, the size of a man's finger.

Flies, Artificial. Fishhook to which colored bits of material, feathers, etc., are attached to vaguely resemble an insect. A few of the 400 odd exotic names for these are: Academy, Armstrong Fontinalis, Blondie, Cupsuptic, Dolly Varden, Emu, Fosnot, Guzzler, Honey Dun, Irish Turkey, Jennie Lind, Killer Diller, Michigan Hopper, Perkin's Pet, Quack Doctor, Telephone Box, and Zulu. If your sportsman is a fly fisherman, any unusual word he uses can be assumed to be the name of a fly.

Flies, Natural. These are the real aquatic insects which

are part of the fish's natural diet. They include May flies, sandflies, stone flies, dobson flies, crane flies, and caddis, and others too numerous for listing. The young are called "nymphs," and the adults are called everything from little blue quills to smokey alders. Their importance is that the fish are jumping when they emerge, any time from April 1 to September 10.

Float Boat. Any small boat (*see* John-Boat), but more often a rubber raft for floating to good fishing areas.

Flounder. A flatfish served in North American restaurants as "filet of sole," since our local soles are not good food fish.

Fluke. Also called summer flounder, but really a halibut.

Fly Books. Device with plastic leaves to hold wet flies, or an aluminum box with small, flat compartments for dry flies.

Fly Boxes. Bulkier than fly books, but made of transparent plastic for easy viewing.

Fly Tying. The art, perfected by professionals and some gifted amateurs, of constructing feathered lures with a handful of materials and tools.

Fry. Young hatch of fish used for stocking lakes and streams.

Gaff Hook. A large hook to land big game fish, or a smaller one to land medium-sized ones.

Gar. Voracious and destructive fish found all over the country, called variously alligator, longnose, shortnose, and spotted gar.

Gigging. Catching fish with four barbless hooks fastened back to back, drawn through a school to catch them in the bodies.

Goldeye. Sometimes called mooneye. A relative of the whitefish and herring, found east of the Mississippi.

Grayling. Game fish similar to trout, found in the Missouri River and the waters of Yellowstone Park, but more abundant in northern Canadian waters.

Grilse. Young salmon, returned for the first time from the sea to fresh water.

Groupers. A large, good-eating fish found mostly in southern waters around Florida and southern California.

Grubs. Larva of insects, good for catching bluegills. Goldenrod are said to be a good source. If your husband follows suggestions of certain authorities, he will hang stems in the basement. Then he will split swellings on stems, remove grubs, and keep several dozen in a Quaker Oats box half full of dry rolled oats. You will, presumably, switch to Wheaties.

Grunion. Small salt-water fish caught on shallow beach by anglers who use only their hands. Found in California.

Guitar Fish. A musical member of the shark class.

Gut. Filament leader derived from the silkworm.

Hackle. A wingless-nymph form of fly, but with more feathering around the head.

Haddock. A North Atlantic food fish allied to the cod, but smaller. Called "finnan haddie" when smoked.

Hake. What my husband says when he wants to swear but there are ladies present. Also a fish abundant in summer off Cape Cod.

Halibut. Large northern flatfish, found in both the Atlantic and Pacific.

Hooks. The instruments on which the fish are caught. Their general classifications are: ringed, eyed, turned up, tapered eye, tapered ring, turned down tapered eye, turned up tapered eye sliced shank, long shank two slices, turned down ball eye four slices, tipped shank bent back, tipped spike bent back, and I think that will be enough of that. Some common names for various types of fish-hooks are: Kirby, Sproat, Pennell, Kinsey, Limerick, Cincinnati Bass, Carlisle, and Treble.

Ice Fly. Fly used to catch fish through ice in winter.

Jack Crevalle. Powerful fighting fish, no good to eat but exciting to catch.

Jigger Fishing. Method of fishing used in Alabama, with a long pole and a short line, using the pole to riffle the water and attract fish.

Jigging. Jerking a small spoon near the bottom to attract fish.

John-Boat. A simple, keelless, flat-bottomed boat used for float fishing.

Kingfish. Strong fish weighing 10 to 50 pounds, plentiful off Florida and South Carolina from November to April.

Leader. A length of gut or nylon used to attach the hook to the line. Leaders were once made of horsehair, and are sometimes made of piano wire. In bait casting they supply strength at the point of wear and tear, and in fly fishing they are less visible to the fish than the line.

Level-Wind. A guide through which the line is threaded so it can be wound on the spool in uniform layers, avoiding the tangling and "mushing" which contribute to back-lash and strong language.

Limnology. The study of the behavior of lakes and other inland waters and the conditions existing in them, which guides the angler in deciding where to fish, how deep to fish, and the approximate kind of tackle to use for best results.

Lines. Monofilament lines are used for spinning. Thermoset is a heat-treated nylon line for bait casting. Coutrai lines are made of linen. Monel metal lines are employed for deep trolling. Enameled or oiled lines are used for fly casting.

Line Dryers. For the unsophisticated fisherman, these can be two chairs between which the line is stretched, if his wife isn't around to interfere. For the gadget lover whose wife objects to falling over fishing lines, these are small reels on which the line can be wound until dry.

LORAN. Long Range Aid to Navigation, or a radio receiver that picks up shore radio signals sent out 24 hours a day by transmitting stations. A good thing for sea fishermen to know about. Inquire U.S. Navy Hydrographic Office, Washington, D.C., or the U.S. Coast Guard.

Lures. Spoons, spinners, plugs, and flies. Spoons and spinners attract the fish with a shining metal blade. Plugs do it by simulating small fish, and flies by simulating insects.

Mackerel. Common mackerel in large schools are off Hatteras in March and April, and off New England in May.

Marlin. One of the speared fishes, like the sailfish, spearfish, and swordfish. Marlin can pierce the oak planking of boats with their spears. The Blue Marlin, found in both the Atlantic and Pacific, weighs between 200 and 300 pounds. Be sure your sportsman takes along a lifebelt and first aid kit when he goes after this one.

Minnow. Any small fish suitable for use as bait. A minnow bucket with an aeration device will keep them alive for a time in a minimum amount of water. Without this, the angler may use the family bathtub, so watch out before you take your next shower in fishing season.

Mooching. A form of spinning used to catch king salmon.

Mossback. A large muskellunge.

Muskellunge. A small mossback.

Pan Fish. Any little fish that can be fried whole.

Panniers. A pair of baskets or trunks designed to be carried on each side of a beast of burden, or possibly a fisherman.

Parr. A young salmon before its first migration seaward.

Perch. Yellow perch are a favorite vacation fish at summer resort lakes and streams. There are also sea perch, silver perch, surf perch, and walleyed perch.

Pickerel. Small members of the pike family. The chain pickerel is the most common, sometimes known as the Eastern pickerel, and Jack or Jackfish. There is also a barred pickerel. The grass pickerel is also sometimes called the mud pickerel.

Pike. The northern pike is a cannibalistic fresh-water fish, found all over the world.

Pirogue. Louisiana boat used for navigating the swamps and streams of the Gulf Coast, once hollowed from a solid log and propelled with paddles or a pushpole, but now constructed of planks and sometimes equipped with an outboard motor.

Pollack. A North Atlantic game fish.

Pompano. A fine-eating and popular sports fish, found mostly on South Atlantic and Gulf coasts.

Popper. A surface-disturbance lure. Some resemble small fish or frogs; others have only a partial body and supplement of feathers, hair, or other material; all have dished heads.

Night-Crawler. Giant worm, four to six inches long, used for bait.

Overhead Cast. Straight-back, straight-forward motion of the rod. The basic cast to learn.

Popping. Casting with any lure which pops when retrieved in hard jerks, attracting fun-loving bass by its noise and splash.

Porgy. A salt-water food fish. Good sport for bottom fishermen.

Pumpkinseed. A beautiful fresh-water fish, also known as sunfish.

Quahog. A hardshell clam used as bait for bottom fish, and fed to summer tourists on Cape Cod and Nantucket.

Rainbow Runner. Fish of striking colors, found most everywhere.

Redeye. A rock bass with a hangover.

Reef Fishing. Fishing in clear water off coral reefs, which has been compared to fishing in an immense aquarium because the view is so clear. Since the medium-sized fish feed on the little ones, and the big fish feed on the medium-sized ones, the sportsman may hook a grunt, then find himself fighting with a grouper, and end up with a shark on the line.

Reel (Automatic). Same as single action but with springs that wind up to supply tension and draw line back on reel spool.

Reel (Salt-Water) These come in both single and multiple action, but carry more line than those for fresh-water fishing.

Reel (Multiplying). Weight of lure pulls line from reel spool, and reel turns several times as crank makes one circle.

Reel (Single Action). A simple, gearless reel with a spool and a crank.

Reel (Spinning). A reel with a spool that does not rotate.

Riffling Fly. A method of fishing in which the wet fly is made to cock to one side so that it skims the surface of the water, leaving a little wake behind it. Used in salmon fishing, originating in Newfoundland.

Rock Bass. A shallow-water fish found over sandy bottom in the vicinity of Monterey, California.

Rock Bass (Fresh Water). A popular pan fish, abundant in small ponds and lakes.

Rockfish. A variety of sea bass, also known as striped bass.

Rod (Fly). A tapered rod with live, springy action.

Rod (Skittering). A long pole, 15 to 20 feet, with a fixed line and live bait lure.

Rod (Spinning). A rod 7 to 8 feet in length, with a long cork grip to which the spinning reel is attached. Tip is stiffer and butt more limber than in a fly rod. Slightly shorter rods are used for spin casting.

Sailfish. Fish with a high, brightly colored dorsal fin which can be folded down into a groove on the back (bet you didn't know that).

Salmon. There are a number of these good-eating game fish. The king salmon is found on the Pacific Coast, and is called, when you buy it in a can, Chinook. The Atlantic salmon is found in streams during migration, and is also known as Kennebec. There is landlocked salmon, also known as Sebago salmon. There is the Sockeye, which often gets itself canned. There is the non-migrating Ouananiche salmon, sometimes called dwarf salmon and often confused with lake trout. With all those aliases, someone is bound to become confused.

Sawfish. A large (800 to 1,000 pounds) fish equipped with a long, flat saw protruding from the upper jaw, with teeth on either side, "the better to eat you with, my dear."

Sculpin. A salt-water fish whose own flesh is highly edible, but whose roe is deadly poison and whose stinger and spines can inflict serious wounds.

Sea Trout. Also known as weakfish. Weighs 1 to 5 lbs., found in channels and inlets, and has been the subject of studies off North Carolina which show that, like the birds, it leaves in the fall and returns in the spring.

Shad. A fish related to the herring, found along the Atlantic coast, which with its roe makes good food.

Shark. An aristocratic fish that can trace its ancestry back millions of years. There are the mako shark with high triangular teeth, the porbeagle shark with small cusps at the base of its teeth, the thresher shark with a long upper tail lobe, and the tiger shark with teeth that are large in front and alike on both jaws. There are also the hammerhead shark, whose head is really shaped like a hammer, with eyes on each end; and the man-eater, or white, shark with serrated teeth. Since some sharks do occasionally eat human beings, Dr. Perry Gilbert of Cornell University takes electrocardiograms of free-swimming sharks to reveal their reaction to chemical repellents. With the right repellent, presumably, the shark will be rendered no more dangerous than a fly.

Sheepshead. A small game fish common from Cape Cod to Tampico.

Shellcracker. One of the largest sunfishes of the South.

Shiner. A minnow.

Sinkers. The purpose of the sinker is to pull the lure down deeper when necessary. Each sinker is suited to the type of fishing to be done, and is usually made of soft lead. The simplest sinker is a small piece of lead or a lead shot with a cut or slot in one side for the line or leader to be inserted. Spindle-shaped sinkers have ears at each end which may be bent to hold the sinker in place. A third type of sinker is a strip of lead wrapped around leader or line spirally. The dipsey sinker is an end-of-the-line sinker, shaped like a cone with a ring at the top.

Snapper. A worldwide fish family of around 200 species. They are called striped pargo, red snapper, silk snapper, cubera, mangrove snapper, dog snapper, schoolmaster snapper, lane snapper, muttonfish snapper, pacific dog snapper, Colorado snapper, jordan's snapper, mullet snapper, spotted rose snapper, and yellowtail.

Snap. A safety pin for fastening a lure or leader.

Snook. A relative of the bass and perch.

Soldier Palmer. A palmer-type fly named for the palmer worm, or caterpillar.

Sole. A non-game fish.

Spear Fishing. Fishing done by means of skin diving and powered spears.

Spinners. A division of the spoon family, constructed

139

with thin blades, usually metal, that whirl around the line of traction. There are single-blade spinners, called Colorado spinners, in which the blade is attached to a split ring to which the hook is also attached. Others have blades that rotate freely around a bearing on a shaft and are called (1) Star-Lowe, (2) Ontario, and (3) Pflueger Bearcat, among others. The Indiana spinner is attached by a "collar" or "saddle." The June Bug is attached to a shaft by a hole or loop bearing. The Flasher or multiple series is a series of spoons with linked shafts. Then there are propeller-blade spinners, with two or more spinners on a shaft rotating in opposite directions. In the Pflueger Cyclone, Buel spinners, and others, other parts of the lure are also rotated by the propeller blades.

Spoons. The oldest of the artificial lures. Their action depends on water resistance to a blade of metal or other material.

Still Fishing. Fishing from the banks of a stream or lake or from an anchored boat, with fresh- or salt-water bait. Russell Baker, of the *New York Times*, describes it in its old-fashioned, nostalgic version: "A time-killer performed along creek banks with a length of twine, a beanpole, ten cents' worth of hooks and a can of worms."

Swivel. A small metal gadget in three parts, to prevent the twisting of one unit in the tackle from being transmitted all along the line.

Swordfish. A large fish with sharp snout and worldwide range, whose steaks are commonly sold in supermarkets.

Tackle. The basic tackle items are: lure, hook, leader, line, reel, and rod. Also included are minor accessories such as sinkers and swivels. Tackle manufacturers bring out new lures each season to tempt the shopping fisherman, just as the hat manufacturers tempt his wife each spring with new chapeaux.

Tarpon. Large game fish found mostly in southern waters, although two have been recorded in Nova Scotia.

Tautog. Also called blackfish, caught from Cape Cod to Delaware, around rocks and seaweed in shallow inshore water.

Trout. Popular game fish found in a number of varieties: lake trout, rainbow trout, brown trout, cutthroat trout, golden trout, brook trout, Dolly Varden trout.

Walleye. A favorite with sportsmen, also known as walleyed pike, walleyed perch, pike perch, and (in Canada) Doré.

Wobbler. A dished-blade spoon with a hole in the forward end. Instead of spinning, the blade is thrown from side to side by the water pressure. There are fixed-hook wobblers, some of which are the Cayuga, the Canadaigua, the Silver Minnow, the Dardevles, and the Pflueger "Record." Others are known as free-swinging hook wobblers, and some of the most popular are called: K-B, Finlander, Old Lob, Oneida, and Onondaga. Typical of the wobbler spoon of the symmetrical, oval-elipse type is the Cayuga. Egg-shaped wobblers come with names like Seneca and others. There are also asymmetrical wobblers, sometimes fish-shaped.

I think I'd better stop here; for if I keep going on like this, you'll soon be saying, like the schoolgirl who wrote in her book report, "This book tells me more about penguins than I want to know"—"This book tells me more about fishing tackle than I want to know!"

11

Speaking the Hunter's Language

◇

◇

◇

When your husband comes home from a hunting trip and tells you that he "bagged his bull," do you know what he's talking about? It means he shot a large male animal, probably a moose. It could mean he shot an elephant, but if he was hunting anywhere in North America, probably not. If he talks about the hard work involved in "dressing it out," he means that he had to remove carefully all the inedible portions of the torso and drag it out of the woods in such a way that the meat would not be bruised—nor the head and antlers injured, if he desired to preserve a trophy. With a heavy animal, this is quite a proposition.

Learning to understand a hunter's vernacular can also be quite a proposition; but here are a few tips on names of common game and the handling and equipment that go into his hunting:

Acme Thunderer. A dog whistle.

Action. The mechanism by which a gun operates.

Alligator. Inhabitant of the Everglades who makes luxury handbags and shoes.

Antelope. The American antelope is known as the "pronghorn" antelope, since it is a horned, not antlered, animal. It is distinctively home-grown, and is not related to any other antelope in the world.

Antlers. Part of the sexual equipment of the male of the deer family, used to fight other males during the rutting season for possession of the females. Also trophies coveted by sportsmen.

Archery. A recently revived sport which has extended into field archery and hunting, with special archery hunting reserves in Oregon, Michigan, Utah, Tennessee, Pennsylvania, and Arizona. Appears to be spreading to other states.

Atlantic Flyway. East Coast migration route of birds.

Autoloader. Once the magazine is loaded, the self-loading gun requires no firing effort other than pulling the trigger for each shot desired.

Automatic. A rapid-firing handgun operated like the autoloader.

Babiche. Rawhide thongs or lacings.

Backpacking. Hiking and carrying a pack on the back for varying distances.

Badger. Small burrowing, nocturnal, carnivorous animal.

Badlands Bighorn. A mountain sheep.

Baiting (Bear). Placing a dead carcass on bear range to attract it. Not considered sporting.

Baldpate. Puddle, or river and pond, duck. Also known as baldcrown, baldhead, and bald widgeon.

Ballistics. The science that deals with the motion of projectiles, like bullets from a gun.

Ball Powder. An ammunition propellant with qualities of uniformity, cleanliness, and chemical stability.

Ball Seater. Loading tool for a muzzle-loading rifle.

Barrel. The tube through which the ammunition is discharged.

Basset. Long-eared, short-legged hound with a deep voice. Popular hunting dog in Belgium and France. Popular television performer in the U. S.

Bay Shooting. Popular kind of waterfowl shooting in Maine where bays and birds are plentiful.

Beagle. Popular hunting dog and family pet of sportsmen and presidents.

Bear. Large, powerful, furry mammal, found in the northern U.S., Canada, and Alaska. The Alaska brown bear is found on the Alaskan Peninsula and Kodiak Island in its largest size of over 1,000 pounds. The black bear comes in cinnamon, blue-gray, and creamy-white, as well as fashionable black. He is found in North Carolina, Tennessee, Florida, and the Rockies, and there are over 150,000 of them. The grizzly is the king of bears and is found in Alaska and the Rockies. The polar bear we all know from seeing him suffer through hot summers at the zoo.

Beaver. An animal whose fur, when sheared and fashioned into coats and jackets, is popular with women. He was nearly trapped to extinction when this country was first settled and men's beaver hats were in vogue. Luckily for us (and the beaver), silk hats eventually took precedence over beaver in men's haberdashery, and the beaver was allowed to survive.

Bench-Rest. A heavy table especially constructed as a solid shooting support, ideally made for testing rifle and ammunition performance.

Bird Fever. Also known as "buck fever," when deer hunting. It is the result of nervous tension which causes the hunter to become almost paralyzed at just the moment when his target is presented to him.

Blind. Hiding-place for a hunter, he optimistically hopes.

Boar. A huge wild swine found in the Great Smokies of North Carolina and eastern Tennessee.

Bobcat. Looks like a large kitten, but don't let that fool you. Also known as bay lynx, red lynx, and wildcat.

Bore. The interior design and diameter of a gun barrel.

Bounty. Outdated idea still practiced in 33 states, by which a reward is paid for killing so-called predatory animals—like fox, coyote, and bobcat—that often do more good than harm. Fox and coyotes feed primarily on unwanted rodents and insects. Bobcats protect the balance of nature by preventing overproduction of the animals they eat, so that they don't starve or become nuisances to man. Bounty is paid in Canada on wolves which kill sick caribou.

Brant. A relative of the European goose, found on U.S. Atlantic coast in winter.

Breech Loader. A firearm loaded by introducing the cartridge or shell at the rear of the barrel.

Brownie. A pistol, a goblin, a flat chocolate cake with nuts, or a junior girl scout.

Browning. A revolver, pistol, shotgun, or poet.

Bufflehead. A North American duck with long head feathers.

Caliber. The internal diameter of the barrel of a gun, expressed in decimals of an inch or millimeters. Also the diameter of a bullet or shell.

Call. An instrument that imitates the cry of a bird or animal.

Canard. A French duck or a false rumor.

Carbine. A light, short-barreled rifle.

Caribou. The most numerous of hoofed big game animals in Alaska. There were once many herds in New England, but all are now gone, due to food shortages, deforestation, and unchecked hunting.

Cartridge. The casing or shell containing primer, powder, wad, and shot or a bullet.

Casting (Bullets). Pouring molten metal into special forms for the manufacture of bullets.

Cat Hound. A dog, frequently of mixed breed, used in hunting lions and other big cats.

Central Flyway. Migration route of birds, just east of the Rockies.

Checkering or Checking. Putting a checked pattern

on a gun stock by means of a special cutting or checkering tool.

Chickaree. Red Squirrel.

Chokebore. A bore narrowed at the muzzle to concentrate the shot.

Clock Shooting. Skeet shooting, or shooting at moving targets that simulate the flight of birds, with the shooter firing from various points around a half-circle.

Cocker Spaniel. Dog used in bird hunting. He finds, flushes, and often retrieves, but does not point. He is also bred for show.

Coney. Rabbit fur that imitates its betters, like mink, chinchilla, etc.

Coonhound. A talkative dog that chases raccoons.

Coot. A ducklike member of the rail and gallinule family. Easily tamed and loves to clown. Hence the expression "Crazy as a coot."

Cormorant. A bird that catches fish and holds them in a pouch. Used in the Orient to catch fish for man.

Cottontail. Easter bunny.

Cougar. A puma.

Covey. A flock of quail or partridge.

Creeps. Not what you think at all; but irregularities in used guns. Also undesirable preliminary movements of the trigger in some guns prior to discharge.

Crows. Intelligent birds who, unfortunately for themselves like to eat the same kinds of crops that feed human beings.

Curlew. A shorebird with long legs and long bill.

Decoys. Likenesses of birds used to trick them into shooting range, since the flying bird sees them and thinks his friends have found feeding grounds, and he doesn't wait to be invited to dinner.

Deer. Familiar animal of which there are several kinds, the blacktail, the mule deer, the whitetail, red deer, and reindeer. The latter have been domesticated by the Eskimos, the Laps, and of course Santa Claus.

Dope Bag. Metal box for carrying score book and pencil, ammunition, forked rifle rest, spotting scope and stand, cartridge block, shooting glove, and anything else necessary for target practice.

Double Gun. Gun with two barrels.

Drive (Deer). Effort by one group of hunters to keep deer moving ahead of them, while another group of "standers" take shots at them (the deer). It is considered the least interesting form of deer hunting.

Ducks. There are 61 kinds of ducks and geese on this continent. There are black ducks, Florida ducks, mallards, pintails, shovelers, several kinds of teal, widgeons, and wood ducks, among those who like rivers and ponds. Among the sea or diving ducks are the canvasback, several kinds of eider, the goldeneye, the harlequin, the Labrador, old squaw, redhead, ringnecked, scaup and scoter.

Ducks Unlimited. A waterfowl conservation association that raises money to conserve and increase waterfowl to look at, to photograph, and to shoot. Most of the money goes to Canada, where duck breeding grounds are to be maintained if the sportsman, photographer and naturalist wish to continue to find their favorite birds in this country.

Elk. Indian name "wapiti," or white deer.

Falconry. The use of hawks or falcons for hunting. The method became obsolete with the introduction of the gun, but has been revived as a sport since 1941, when the American Falconers' Association was formed.

Ferret. A black-footed weasel.

Field Trials. Competitive tests of hunting dogs in the field, or indoors in an approximation of field conditions.

Flintlock. An obsolete firearm in which a flint was used to ignite the powder in the pan.

Fox. Small, wild, canine mammal, the red variety of which is hunted for sport, while the grey makes fluffy trimming for glamorous clothes.

Foxhound. A hound that chases foxes in the U.S., in imitation of his upper class English relatives.

Gallery Range. This rifle range can be set up in almost any large cellar or basement, so watch out!

Gauge. The diameter of the bore of a shotgun.

Glasses (Shooting). Binoculars.

Goose. Those found in our area in the fall are barnacle goose, blue goose, Canada goose (common, western, and lesser), cackling goose, Richardson's (Hutchins') goose, emperor goose, Ross's goose, greater snow goose, lesser snow goose, tule goose, white-fronted goose, and American brant.

Grouse. A relative of the pheasant and farmyard chicken.

Guns. What a sportsman gets his game with, unless he is an archer or a falconer. Usually identified by name and model number.

Gunsling. A long, folded strap attached to a rifle and intended as an aid in aiming. Also used to carry the rifle.

Handguns. Revolvers and automatic pistols.

Handloading. The do-it-yourself method of assembling or reloading cartridges or shotgun shells at home.

Hares. Rodent-like mammals allied to rabbits but larger.

Harrier. A small hound used for hunting hares. Also a marsh hawk.

Hawks. Birds of prey active in the daytime, some of which are trained for use in falconry.

Heel. What a dog does when he comes to an attendant position close beside but slightly behind the hunter.

Hibernation. Act of passing the winter in a dormant state. Said to be true of black, brown, and polar bears, blue grouse, muskrats, opossums, prairie dogs, raccoons, skunks, squirrels, and woodchucks.

Hides. Skins of animals, sometimes preserved or tanned by stretching, tumbling, and sandpapering, whence the expression "Tan your hide."

Hooter Hunting. Shooting blue grouse when they are booming out a summons to their harems. Outlawed as unsporting.

Hounds. Hunting dogs, especially those who hunt by scent and in packs. There are the basset, the beagle, the black and tan coon, the plott, the trigg hound, walker hound, and many others, besides the foxhounds.

Hurlbutt (Mrs. Gertrude). The originator of the name "skeet" for that type of shooting.

Intermediate Refuges. Refuge areas for the rest and refreshment of waterfowl on their flights to and from nesting and wintering refuges.

Jaguar. A large, tawny, spotted feline of Central America, and a small, sporty, expensive automobile of Great Britain.

Jesses. Short straps on each leg of a hawk, used for attaching to the leash.

Jill. A female ferret. The male is called a "Hob."

Kestrel. A sparrow hawk.

Kneeling Position. A position in rifle shooting, with right foot under buttocks and left elbow resting on left knee. Not to be attempted until the rifleman has become a good shot in prone (flat on stomach) and sitting (an elbow resting on each knee) positions.

Kublai Khan. A great Mongolian emperor who forbade the killing of pheasants and entertained Marco Polo—but presumably not with a pheasant dinner.

Lapstreak Float. A boat built of planks overlapping and fastened together.

Laughing Goose. The one that got away.

Laughing Mallard. See above.

Leading (Barrel). What happens when a gun barrel gets badly streaked with lead and no longer shoots accurately.

Lean-to. A crude hut or shelter, sloping to the ground from a raised support.

Ledge Shooting. Shooting from long points of land exposed at half-tide, popular in Maine where such spots are abundant.

Lever-Action. A flat, compact rifle with lever beneath the stock. Lever-action shotguns are no longer used.

Live-Trapping. A harmless method of catching animals, employed by game management and conservation officials.

Lure. A bunch of feathers and bait on a long cord, used to recall a hawk in the practice of falconry.

Lynx. A wildcat with short tail, tufted ears, and long legs. Also known as Canada lynx, bay lynx, and bobcat.

Machete. A heavy knife used as an implement or weapon

Mad Moon. Period in early fall when grouse go on wild flights, bumping into buildings, light wires, radio towers, telephone poles, and automobile windshields.

Magazine. Part of a gun holding extra rounds of ammunition ready for successive shots.

Magnum. A term identifying the most high-powered guns and cartridges within each family of calibers or gauges.

Mallard. Common wild duck, ancestor of domestic breeds. During the 1964-65 New York World's Fair, a domestic Long Island duck left the farm and joined his relatives on a trip to the lake at the Fair, where the fountain displays were held. He was soon deserted, when their migrating instincts took the others south.

Marksmanship. Skill in hitting the mark which, if he is successful at it, gives your sportsman oneupmanship over his less skilled competitors.

Marmot. Genus of rodent including the woodchuck, the yellow-bellied marmot, and the hoary or whistling marmot.

Marsupials. Opossums and kangaroos both belong to this order of animal, in which the female lacks a placenta and must carry its undeveloped young in a pouchlike receptacle on the abdomen.

Marten. A weasel-like carnivorous animal, with valuable dark-brown fur that makes attractive neckpieces.

Speaking the Hunter's Language

Matchlock. An old-fashioned musket fired by igniting the powder with a slow-burning wick or match.

Match Rifles. Rifles especially designed for shooting in competitive matches.

Mauser. A rifle, a form of rifle action, or an automatic pistol named after P. S. Mauser, German inventor, who died in 1914.

Merganser. A fish-eating, diving duck with serrated bill.

Migration. Moving seasonally from one location to another, as birds, fish, deer, elk, sheep, and people who can afford to winter in Miami, Fla.

Mink. You need a definition?

Mississippi Flyway. Migratory route of the blue goose, blue-winged teal, Canada goose, redhead, ringnecked duck, and shoveler, to name but a few.

Moose. A large mammal of the deer family, whose broad, flat antlers have finger-like projections and whose big, flapping ears often carry the stamp of the U.S. Fish and Wildlife Service, which is interested in following his migrations.

Musk Ox. He is shaggy and hollow-horned, and combines the features of the sheep and the goat. Despite his name, he is not an ox, and he doesn't smell of musk; but his underwool makes lightweight, warm sweaters, and he was nearly exterminated for this cozy winter underwear of his.

Muskrat. The working girl's mink.

Muzzle-Loaders. Guns loaded through the muzzle (what else?).

Okefenokee. A swamp and animal refuge in South Georgia and North Florida, where there are black bear, alligator, deer, and bobcats, as well as rabbits, ducks, geese, and cranes. Also the home of Pogo and his friends.

Open Seasons. Seasons when hunting is legally permitted.

Opossum. Animal noted for feigning death when threatened. Thus the expression "Playing possum."

Otter. A webfooted, aquatic mammal related to the weasel, which makes a good pet if you have an estate complete with swimming pool or a duplex with an extra-large bathtub.

Overshooting. Shooting too high at the target. Sometimes shooting too low at a descending duck or other descending target.

Owl. Bird with eyes set to look in the same direction, so he must turn his head around to see. They are nocturnal hunters of mice, other small rodents, and some birds. They come in a number of sizes and markings, from the barred owl, spotted owl, burrowing owl, elf owl, and great gray owl to the horned owl, long-eared owl, pygmy owl, Richardson's owl, saw-whet owl, barn owl, snowy owl, screech owl, and short-eared owl. They are not particularly wise. Just look that way.

Pacific Flyway. Migratory route of waterfowl along the Pacific Coast of the United States and Canada.

Packboard. Board used to support backpack gear and keep it from rubbing against the body.

Palmetto Jumper. A combination dog-lunch-shooting-truck for use on the palmetto barrens of Florida. The shooters ride on top, while the dogs range ahead.

Panniers. Baskets slung on both sides of a beast of

burden, as on the donkey so frequently depicted in Mexican scenes.

Partridge. Small, plump game birds.

Patches. Material for cleaning and loading guns.

Peregrine Falcon. Duck hawk.

Pheasant. Long-tailed, beautifully plumaged, Asian bird. The ring-necked pheasant is widely bred in the United States.

Pigeons and Doves. The domestic pigeon is square-tailed. It used to sit on rocks, but now decorates buildings and statues. The mourning dove has a pointed tail, is considered a songbird in the north and a game bird in the south, where it is more plentiful. The band-tailed pigeon and white-winged dove are two more game birds in the family. The passenger pigeon was exterminated by mass killing for the market.

Pistol. A small firearm of the automatic type. Sometimes also includes revolvers. There are single-shot, double-barreled, multiple-barreled, repeating, and semi-automatic pistols.

Plover. Shore birds, with long, pointed wings and short tails, and their relatives in the uplands. Some are becoming rare because of human encroachments on their breeding grounds.

Pointer. A short-haired brown, black, or lemon and white dog, trained to scent and point game, and often to compete in field trials. Three have won the National Championship three times: Mary Montrose, Becky Broomhill, and Ariel. If human beings were bred as carefully as these dogs, we would be a race of supermen and superwomen.

Polecat. A skunk by any other name would smell as sweet.

Poodle. Short for pudelhund (water dog). Can be used with success to retrieve ducks, but more often merely decorative.

Porcupine. A large rodent, covered with erectile quills that are difficult to remove from the flesh.

Powder. Gunpowder. Thus U.S. slang "To take a powder," meaning to depart precipitously.

Predator. Animal that lives by preying on others. Part of nature's plan to prevent overpopulation and consequent starvation of the preyed-on species. Extinction of predators by human beings with kindly motives often has disastrous results.

Preserve. Area set aside for the protection of wildlife, or restricted for private hunting or fishing.

Pronghorn. American animal resembling an antelope.

Ptarmigan. A species of grouse in white winter camouflage.

Quail. Bobwhite quail (also called bob-white, partridge, quail, Virginia partridge). Other members of the family are the desert, massena, mountain, scaled, or valley quail. Whatever you call him, he's a favorite upland game bird.

Rabbit. The animal responsible for hasenpfeffer and cheap fur coats.

Raccoon. Animal with dainty little forepaws that look like hands, which he often uses to dunk his food carefully in water before eating.

Rail. Long-legged, short-winged bird with turned-up tail.

Recoil. Backward movement of gun at moment of firing, responsible for many bruised shoulders.

Refuges. Places where game are given proper protection so that they can grow and replenish themselves. Where wildlife has not shrunk beyond the danger point, it can be increased once more by preserving natural habitats.

Remington. Important arms manufacturer.

Retriever. Dog bred to retrieve game: Chesapeake Bay, curly-coated, Labrador, etc.

Revolver. Pistol with revolving cylinder.

Rifle. A gun with a much longer effective range than a shotgun, partly because of the spiral grooves in the bore.

Rucksack. Canvas knapsack.

Scaup. Sea duck related to the canvasback.

Scoter. Sea duck with bill swollen at the base.

Setter. Silky-coated, long-haired game dog that indicates presence of quarry by standing rigid.

Sheep. Animal responsible for mouton coats.

Shotgun. A smoothbore gun, single- or double-barreled.

Sights. Focusing devices to assist aim of gun.

Skeet. A form of shotgun practice, shooting at a succession of targets fired at from various angles.

Sneak Boat or Sneak Box. Small, shallow craft used as a combination boat and blind for duck hunting.

Snipe. Long-billed shore or marsh birds related to the woodcock.

Spaniel. Dog with long ears and long, silky hair. Good retriever and popular pet.

Stalking. Approaching game stealthily.

Telescope Sights. Sights incorporating glass lens for long-distance shooting or hunting.

Tracking or Trailing. Following game by its footprints or other indications.

Trophy. That moosehead hanging in the family room.

Undershooting. Shooting short of or below the mark.

Upland. Interior, as opposed to shore.

Varmint (Vermin). Animal considered injurious to other game, crops, or livestock.

Weasel. Small carnivore with brownish fur. He turns white in winter, with black-tipped tail, and is then more elegantly known as ermine.

Whooping Crane. Nearly extinct birds, of which there are thirty-odd being carefully protected at Great Slave Lake in Canada in summer and in the Aransas National Wildlife Refuge, Texas, in winter. They fly across Alberta and Saskatchewan, then down through the Dakotas, Nebraska, Kansas, Missouri, Arkansas, Oklahoma, and into Texas. Hunters along the route are cautioned not to shoot at them. They are easily recognized by their large size, black-tipped wings and red-crowned heads.

Widgeon. Short-billed river duck.

Winchester. Famous arms manufacturer.

Wolf. Dog-like animal, hunted by man and reputed to make a dependable mate. Or a man who hunts women and makes a thoroughly undependable mate.

Woodchuck. The ground hog who sees his shadow and foretells the coming of spring.

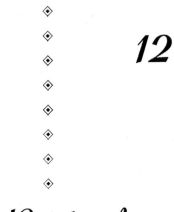

12

Read Any Outdoor Books Lately?

Books about the outdoors and animal life are very popular among readers today. Every publisher knows that if he gets out a human interest book about a couple who made good in the woods, or a person with a cute wild animal pet, he's all set for some rewarding sales that will make up for that loss he's taking on a slim volume of poetry written by his wife's second cousin.

While you may not have sufficient personal interest in hunting or fishing to care to read technical books, which are aimed at male readership anyway, there are all sorts of books—both paperback and hardcover—on the related subjects of nature, dogs, wild animals, and birds. That these topics are of interest to women is self-evident, since women are the principal book-buyers. And each season sees a book of this sort on the best-seller list.

EVERYBODY'S READING THEM

Grizzlies in Their Back Yard, by Beth Day (New York: Julian Messner, Inc., 1956), was one of these, which told about a couple who left a humdrum life in Seattle for adventures in British Columbia among the grizzly bears. After that, there was a book by a Canadian Mounty's wife, who described her life in the wilds. Currently there is a paperback by Marjorie Michael, called *I Married a Hunter* (Pyramid, 1964), which should find sympathetic female readers.

The *National Geographic* discovered years ago the appeal of the outdoors, and its magazine is still going strong. *National Wildlife* Magazine, published by the National Wildlife Federation, and *Natural History* Magazine, published by the American Museum of Natural History, are two more publications that appeal to the nature lover in most of us. *Outdoor Life, Sports Afield,* and *Field and Stream* are three publications dealing directly with hunting and fishing, and so are more specialized—but you can always find some article in each issue with a measure of feminine appeal. For instance, one number of *Outdoor Life* (April, 1964) has a piece by Bob Cary, called "Blizzard Bass," with some intriguing pictures of his wife, Lil, catching a smallmouth in the Minnesota lake country.

Read Any Outdoor Books Lately?

Sports Afield (January, 1964) goes *Outdoor Life* one better, with an amusing fiction story about a father who gives his teen-age daughter a fly-tying kit for her fifteenth birthday. An issue of *Field and Stream* (July, 1963) contains an article of interest to parents, on teaching a twelve-year-old girl how to handle a shotgun so that she may become a markswoman. If your husband happens to be a subscriber to one of these publications, thumb through an issue now and again. A subscription of your own to one of the more general outdoor magazines will also be rewarding, as they are profusely illustrated with color photographs from all over the country and the world. If you are an armchair adventurer, then *National Geographic* is for you. If you are an amateur naturalist, perhaps *Natural History* Magazine would be better suited to your tastes. For the woman who likes to sponsor causes, *National Wildlife* is the answer, since their by-word is conservation, and they tell how it can be accomplished both nationally and locally. They also enlist the co-operation of the hunter and the fisherman, since conservation helps us all, whether we are thinking in terms of sport, recreation, beauty, or simply preservation of our national heritage.

If you are a television viewer as well as a reader, you can become more closely acquainted with the outdoors through the nature movies of Walt Disney and the "Wild Kingdom" TV programs of zoologist Marlin Perkins or "Zoorama" with Bob Dale. There are also shows like "Flying Fisherman," about game fish in the Gulf of Mexico or large mouth bass in Florida, and "The American Sportsman" series, with Robert Stack hunting elephants in Africa and Kirk Douglas hunting tiger in India.

PICK YOUR CATEGORY

There are a number of types of books on the outdoors. There are those by people who have made pets of wild animals, like Joy Adamson; others by men who catch wild animals alive for zoos, such as Gerald Durrell; and still others by observers of the natural scene, such as John Kieran. A fourth category is the traveler-adventurer or traveler-scientist; a fifth, the couple who take to the wilds; and a sixth, the writer of animal fiction. I'll try to list some of these for you in a way that will make for easy selection of the kind you think you'd prefer.

Wild Animal Pets (Paperback)

BORN FREE *(lions)*, Joy Adamson, Macfadden Publications.

FOREVER FREE, Joy Adamson, Macfadden Publications.

RASCAL *(raccoon)*, Sterling North, Avon Books.

RING OF BRIGHT WATER *(otters)*, Gavin Maxwell, Crest Books.

SEAL MORNING *(seals)*, Rowena Farre, Ace Publications.

EAGLE IN THE BATHTUB *(eagle)*, Jule Mannix, Ballantine Books.

Wild Animal Pets (Hardcover)

ALL THINGS BOTH GREAT & SMALL *(eagles, falcons, etc.)*, Daniel P. Mannix, McGraw Hill Co.

GARA-YAKA *(cheetah)*, Desmond Varaday, E. P. Dutton Co.

TUPU-TUPU-TUPU *(wolverines, love interest)*, Peter Krott, Hutchinson & Co.

KANGAROOS IN THE KITCHEN, Lorrain D'Essen, David McKay Co.

Read Any Outdoor Books Lately?

I WENT TO THE WOODS *(owls, eagles, hummingbirds, and falcons)*, Ronald Austing. Obtainable from National Wildlife Magazine, 1412 16th St. N.W., Washington, D.C. 20036.

Catching Them Alive (Paperback)

BAFUT BEAGLES, Gerald Durell, Ballantine Books *(amusing)*.

OVERLOADED ARK, Gerald Durell, Ballantine Books *(amusing)*.

THREE TICKETS TO ADVENTURE, Gerald Durell, Berkley Publications.

Catching Them Alive (Hardcover)

ISLAND ZOO, Gerald Durell, Macrae Smith.

OPERATION NOAH, Charles Lagus, Coward-McCann *(rescue of wild animals in Africa stranded on islands in lake formed by a dam)*.

THE CRY OF A BIRD, Dorothy Yglesias, E. P. Dutton *(rescue of injured seabirds on British Coast)*.

BRING 'EM BACK ALIVE, Frank Buck, Grosset & Dunlap, Inc.

ON JUNGLE TRAILS, Frank Buck, Lippincott.

Nature Observations (Paperback)

HERD OF RED DEER, F. Fraser Darling, Natural History Library.

HUMAN SIDE OF ANIMALS, Vance Packard, Pocket Books.

MAN AND DOLPHIN, John C. Lilly, M.D., Worlds of Science.

NATURALIST IN ALASKA, Adolph Murie, New Home Library.

PUMA: MYSTERIOUS AMERICAN CAT, Stanley P. Young and Edw. A. Goldman, Dover Books.

THIS FASCINATING ANIMAL WORLD, Alan Devoe, McGraw-Hill Co.

THE SEA AROUND US, Rachel Carson, Houghton Mifflin Co.

SILENT SPRING, Rachel Carson, Houghton Mifflin Co.

ADVENTURES IN NATURE, Edwin Way Teale, Apollo Editions.

DESERT YEAR, Joseph Wood Krutch, Compass Books. (Perhaps you caught his great television program on this subject.)

GRAND CANYON, Joseph Wood Krutch, Anchor Books.

JOHN BURROUGH'S AMERICA, Farida Wiley, New Home Library. (Miss Wiley is a wonderful naturalist, with a lively approach to the subject.)

OCEAN ISLAND *(Inagua)*, Gilbert Klingel, Anchor Books *(the land of the flamingo)*.

OF MEN AND MOUNTAINS, William O. Douglas, Athenium.

THEODORE ROOSEVELT'S AMERICA, Theodore Roosevelt (Farida Wiley, editor), New Home Library.

TWELVE SEASONS, Joseph Wood Krutch, Apollo Editions.

THE FLOWERING EARTH, Donald Culross Peattie, Viking Explorer Books.

Nature Observations (Hardcover)

EVERYMAN'S ARK, Sally P. Johnson, Harper Bros.

STRANGE ANIMALS I HAVE KNOWN, Raymond L. Ditmars, Harcourt, Brace & World.

NATURAL HISTORY OF NEW YORK CITY, John Kieran, Houghton Mifflin.

Read Any Outdoor Books Lately?

NOT UNDER OATH, John Kieran, Houghton Mifflin.

ANIMALS AND OTHER PEOPLE, Louis Bromfield, Harper Bros.

UNSEEN LIFE OF NEW YORK, William Beebe, Duell, Sloan & Pierce.

LITTLE WONDERS OF NATURE, Per Hafslund, Lyle Stuart, Inc.

THE WORLD OF THE BEAVER, Leonard Lee Rue, Lippincott.

ONE DAY AT TETON MARSH, Sally Carrighan, Knopf.

ONE DAY ON BEETLE ROCK, Sally Carrighan, Knopf.

HOME IS THE DESERT, Ann Woodin, The Macmillan Co.

IF YOU DON'T MIND MY SAYING SO, Joseph Wood Krutch, Sloane.

THE LIVING WILDERNESS, Rutherford G. Montgomery, Dodd, Mead Co.

THE FIELDS OF NOON, Sheila Burnford (author of THE INCREDIBLE JOURNEY), Atlantic Monthly Press.

THE UNNATURAL ENEMY, Vance Bourjally, Dial Press *(study of the psychology of the hunter and the hunted)*.

WORLD OF ANIMALS, Joseph Wood Krutch, Simon & Schuster.

ANIMAL WORLDS, Marston Bates, Random House *(struggle for survival)*.

Traveler-Adventurer-Scientist (Paperback)

ANIMAL TREASURE, Ivan T. Sanderson, Viking Explorer Books.

AMERICA BY CAR, Norman D. Ford, Crown Publications.

CALIFORNIA'S BACK COUNTRY (The Mountains and Trails

of Santa Barbara County), Dick Smith and Frank Van
Schaick, Rand McNally.

EXPLORING THE LITTLE RIVERS OF NEW JERSEY, James and
Margaret Cawley, Rutgers Univ. Press.

GREAT ADVENTURES IN SMALL BOATS, David Klein and
Mary Louise King, Collier Books.

GREEN HILLS OF AFRICA, Ernest Hemingway, Scribner's.

MY FAMILY AND OTHER ANIMALS, Gerald Durell, Compass Books.

EXCURSIONS, Henry D. Thoreau, Corinth Citadel.

Travel-Adventurer-Scientist (Hardcover)

WILD LIVES OF AFRICA, Juliette Huxley, Harper & Row
(journey across Africa with husband, Julian).

A SENTIMENTAL SAFARI, Kermit Roosevelt, Knopf *(re-enactment of TR's big game hunt of 1909).*

JEOPARDY AND A JEEP, Dorothy Rogers, Richard R. Smith.

I MARRIED ADVENTURE, Osa Johnson, Lippincott *(photographing wild animals with husband, Martin).*

Couples in the Wilds (Hardcover)

GRIZZLIES IN THEIR BACK YARD, Beth Day, Julian Messner.

WE LIKE IT WILD, Bradford Angier, Stackpole Books *(a husband and wife in the Canadian Rockies).*

THE CHEECHAKOES, Wayne Short, available from National Wildlife Co. *(husband, wife, and three teen-age sons leave Colorado for Alaska).*

ROADLESS AREA, Paul and Susan Brooks, available from
National Wildlife Co. *(husband and wife on wading, portaging and paddling trips).*

Read Any Outdoor Books Lately?

Animal Fiction and Humor (Paperback)

GENTLE ANNIE, MacKinlay Kantor, Popular Publications *(story of a hunting dog)*.

THE GUNTOTER AND OTHER STORIES OF THE MISSOURI HILLS, MacKinlay Kantor, Signet Publications.

FISHING FOR LAUGHS, Hal Sherman, Ace Publications *(cartoons)*.

THE SELF-MADE MAD, Signet Publications *(fishing and boating cartoons)*.

HOW TO TELL THE BIRDS FROM THE FLOWERS, Robt. Williams Wood, Dover Publications.

Animal Fiction and Humor (Hardcover)

THE HAWK IS HUMMING, George Mendoza, Bobbs-Merrill *(shark killer and romance on the coast of Maine)*.

JAYBIRDS GO TO HELL ON FRIDAY, Havilah Babcock, Holt, Rinehart & Winston *(sixteen hunting and fishing stories)*.

THE SNOWS OF KILIMANJARO, & OTHER STORIES, Ernest Hemingway, Scribner.

THE OLD MAN AND THE SEA, Ernest Hemingway, Scribner.

AGED IN THE WOODS, Paul H. Bonner, Scribner.

SHOTS HEARD ROUND THE WORLD, Ellis O. Briggs, Viking.

TO HELL WITH HUNTING, Ed Zern, Meredith Publications.

HUNTING ANYONE? Syd Hoff, Bobbs-Merrill.

TO HELL WITH FISHING, Harold T. Webster, Ed Zern, Meredith Publications.

THE FISH IN MY LIFE, Murray Hoyt, Crown Publications (stories from *Sports Illustrated* and *Saturday Evening Post*).

THE POND, Robert Murphy, E. P. Dutton & Co. (best seller and Animal Book Award Winner).

Cookbooks (Paperback)

For more practical purposes, here are a few of the best fish and game cookbooks:

FISH AND SEAFOOD COOKBOOK, Barbara Fried, Collier Books.

OUTDOORSMAN'S COOKBOOK, Arthur Carhart, Collier Books.

PHEASANTS FOR PEASANTS, Selena Royale and George Renavent, Ward Ritchie Press.

VENISON BOOK, Audrey Alley Gorton, Stephen Greene Press.

GAME IS GOOD EATING, John Willard, State Publishing Co., Helena, Mont.

Cookbooks (Hardcover)

GAME COOKING, Theodora Fitzgibbon, Andre Deutsch.

GREAT DISHES OF THE WORLD, Robert Carrier, Random House.

EVERY SPORTSMAN'S COOKBOOK, National Wildlife Federation Book Service.

WILDERNESS COOKERY, Bradford Angier, Stackpole Books.

STALKING THE BLUE-EYED SCALLOP, Ewell Gibson, National Wildlife.

Guidebooks (Paperback)

For instructive reading, there are any number of good guidebooks in the nature field:

Read Any Outdoor Books Lately?

RACCOON FAMILY PETS, Leonore Brandt, Alpet Publications.

SKUNKS AS PETS, Charles Hume, Alpet Publications.

COMMON NATIVE ANIMALS, M. F. Vessel and E. J. Harrington, Chandler Publishing Co.

FLORIDA FISH AND FISHING, Gordon Lewis, Great Outdoors Publishing Co.

HOW TO KNOW THE AMERICAN MAMMALS, Ivan T. Sanderson, New American Library.

HOW TO KNOW THE BIRDS, Roger Tory Peterson, Signet Key Books.

OUR SMALL NATIVE ANIMALS, Robert Snedigar, Dover Press.

GAMEBIRDS, Dr. Herbert S. Zim, Golden Books.

GUIDE TO AMERICAN WATERFOWL, Hunter's Encyclopedia Staff, Collier Books.

INTRODUCTION TO BIRD LIFE FOR BIRD WATCHERS, Aretas A. Saunders, Dover Press.

LIFE HISTORIES OF NORTH AMERICAN BIRDS OF PREY, Arthur Cleveland Bent, Dover Press.

LIFE HISTORIES OF NORTH AMERICAN DIVING BIRDS, Arthur Cleveland Bent, Dover Press.

LIFE HISTORIES OF NORTH AMERICAN WILD FOWL, Arthur Cleveland Bent, Dover Press.

MULTITUDE OF LIVING THINGS, Lorus J. and Margery J. Milne, Apollo Editions.

OUR NATIONAL PARKS, Monroe Heath, Pacific Coast Publications.

GREAT AMERICAN MOUNTAINS, Monroe Heath, Pacific Coast Books.

GREAT AMERICAN RIVERS AT A GLANCE, Monroe Heath, Pacific Coast Books.

Guidebooks (Hardcover)

OUTDOOR REFERENCE GUIDE, Amelia Reynolds Long, Stackpole Books.

THE BOOK OF WILD PETS, Clifford B. Moore, Branford Publications.

FIELD GUIDE TO THE BIRDS (EASTERN), Roger Tory Peterson, Houghton Mifflin Co.

FIELD GUIDE TO THE BIRDS (WESTERN), Roger Tory Peterson, Houghton Mifflin Co.

SONG AND GARDEN BIRDS OF NORTH AMERICA, National Geographic Society.

SOME GOOD TITLES FOR BOYS

There are many wives with no personal interest in fishing and hunting, who would nevertheless like to interest the children in the hobby. Here are a few juvenile books that will be helpful.

Juveniles (Paperback)

FISHING FOR BOYS, Tom McNally, Follett Publishing Co.

HUNTING FOR BOYS, Tom McNally, Follett Publishing Co.

FIRST CAMPING TRIP, C. B. Colby, Scholastic Book Services.

FIRST JUNGLE BOOK, Rudyard Kipling, Scholastic Book Services.

FISHING, Merit Badge Series, Boy Scouts of America.

Read Any Outdoor Books Lately?

Juveniles (Hardcover)

THE GRIZZLY *(fiction)* Annabel and Edgar Johnson, Harper & Row.

BOYS' COMPLETE BOOK OF FRESH & SALT WATER FISHING, H. P. Rodman and Edward C. Janes, Oliver Publications.

THE BOY'S BOOK OF RIFLES, Charles E. Chapel, Coward-McCann, Inc.

You will note the emphasis on boys in the matter of hunting and fishing books. How can society expect a wife to be sympathetic toward a sportsman's hobby when she has had, from childhood, so little opportunity to learn its attractions? After looking through some recent Girl Scout Handbooks, the only references to fishing and hunting I found were directions on how to tie a fisherman's knot and how to build a hunter's fire.

BOOKS FOR INDIFFERENT WOMEN

The Girl Scouts and Camp Fire Girls do acquaint female children with nature, of course. Most of us love nature, or imagine we do. But there are some diehards who find nature in the raw distasteful; and for them the only attraction about fishing would be a fine-looking boat, and the only saving grace of hunting would be the attractive hunting dogs—and of course, the hunters.

Books About Boats (Paperback)

ABC'S OF SMALL BOAT SAILING, Alice and Lincoln Clark, Doubleday.

COLLIER QUICK & EASY GUIDE TO MOTOR BOATING, Robt. Scharff, Collier Books.

COMPACT BOOK OF BOATING, Jack Seville, J. Lowell Pratt.

COMPLETE BOOK OF BOATING & SAILING, Philip Handleman, Bantam Books.

CRUISING, Peter Heaton, Penguin Books.

CRUISING GUIDE, Brandt Aymar and John Marshall, Chilton Books.

LEARNING TO SAIL IS FUN, George O'Day, Grosset & Dunlap.

OUTBOARDING MADE EASY FOR THE BOAT OWNER, John D. Lenk, John F. Rider.

POWER BOATS, Bill Wallace, Golden Books.

Books About Dogs (Paperback)

ALL ABOUT DOGS, Beth Brown, Collier Books.

ANIMAL STREET: AN ANTHOLOGY, Beth Brown, Collier Books.

DOGS, A TO Z, Edwin Megargee, Grosset & Dunlap.

HUNTING DOGS AND THEIR USES, Stackpole Books.

STERLING BOOK OF DOGS, Robert V. Masters, Sterling Publications.

INCREDIBLE JOURNEY (*fiction*), Sheila Bunford, Bantam Books.

LASSIE COME HOME (*fiction*), Eric Knight, Tempo Publications.

Books About Dogs (Hardcover)

THE THINKING DOG'S MAN, by Ted Patrick, National Wildlife Book Service.

FIFTY YEARS IN THE DOGHOUSE, Lloyd Alexander, National Wildlife Book Service.

Read Any Outdoor Books Lately?

THE JOEY STORY, Rosanna Phelps Warren, Random House.

LOVE ON A LEASH, Kurt Unkelbach, Prentice-Hall.

GIFT BOOKS FOR YOUR SPORTSMAN

In most families the women do the major part of the reading. However, given a book on his favorite subject, a man will rediscover his ability to read. One of the following might make a pleasant surprise gift:

Hunting Books (Paperback)

COLLIER QUICK & EASY GUIDE TO HUNTING, Robert Scharff, Collier Books.

COLLIER BOOK OF HUNTING, Jim Rikhof, J. Lowell Pratt.

FUNDAMENTALS OF FISHING & HUNTING, Byron Dalrymple, Permabooks.

LAW FOR THE SPORTSMAN, Robt. Debevec, Oceana Publications.

HOW TO HUNT DEER, Edward A. Freeman, Collier Books.

OUTDOOR LIFE SHOOTING BOOK, Jack O'Connor, Grosset & Dunlap.

SPORTSMAN'S DIGEST OF HUNTING, Hal Sharp, Barnes & Noble.

TRAINING HUNTING DOGS, Hunter's Encyclopedia Staff, Collier Books.

UPLAND GAME & GUNNING, Hunter's Encyclopedia Staff, Collier Books.

UPLAND GAME HUNTER'S BIBLE, Dan Holland, Doubleday.

VARMINT AND CROW HUNTER'S BIBLE, Bert Popowski, Doubleday.

WILD FOWL DECOYS, Joel Barber, Dover Press.

Enjoying Life as a Sportsman's Wife

Hunting Books (Hardcover)

LIVES OF GAME ANIMALS, Ernest Thompson Seton, Branford Publications *(eight-volume set)*.

BOWHUNTING FOR DEER, H. R. Wambold, Stackpole Books.

HUNTING DUCKS AND GEESE, Edward C. Janes, Stackpole Books.

HUNTING MEDIUM SIZED GAME, Clyde Ormond, Stackpole Books.

HUNTING OUR BIGGEST GAME, Clyde Ormond, Stackpole Books.

THE DEER HUNTER'S GUIDE, Francis E. Sell, Stackpole Books.

THE HUNTER'S ENCYCLOPEDIA, Editor, Raymond R. Camp, Stackpole Books.

FIELD & STREAM SPORTSMAN'S WORLD, Holt, Rinehart & Winston.

SPORTSMAN'S COUNTRY, Donald Culross Peattie, Houghton Mifflin.

SMALL GAME HUNTING, Francis E. Sell, Stackpole Books.

Gun Books (Paperback)

GUN DIGEST TREASURY, John T. Amber, Follett Publishing Co.

14 OLD GUN CATALOGS, L. D. Satterlee, Follett Publishing Co.

PRACTICAL BOOK OF AMERICAN GUNS, John Houston Craige, Collier Books.

RIFLE SHOOTING, Hunter's Encyclopedia Staff, Collier Books.

SHOOTER'S BIBLE TREASURY, John Olson, Follett Publishing Co.

SHOTGUNS & SHOTGUN SHOOTING, Hunter's Encyclopedia Staff, Collier Books.

Gun Books (Hardcover)

THE AMERICAN SHOTGUNNER, Francis Sell, Stackpole Books.

THE COLLECTING OF GUNS, James E. Serven, Stackpole Books.

THE PISTOL SHOOTER'S BOOK, Charles Askins, Stackpole Books.

SIXGUNS, Elmer Keith, Stackpole Books.

THE RIFLE BOOK, Jack O'Connor, Alfred Knopf.

SHOTGUNNER'S BOOK, Charles Askins, Stackpole Books.

SHOTGUNS BY KEITH, Elmer Keith, Stackpole Books.

BIG GAME RIFLES & CARTRIDGES, Elmer Keith, Stackpole Books.

RIFLES, A MODERN ENCYCLOPEDIA, Henry M. Stebbins, Stackpole Books.

Fishing Books (Paperback)

COMPACT BOOK OF FRESH WATER FISHING, Bob Swirz, J. Lowell Pratt.

COMPLETE GUIDE TO SPIN-FISHING, Ray Ovington, Cornerstone Library.

FISHERMAN'S DIGEST, Tom McNally, Follett.

FISHERMEN'S HANDBOOK, Rube Allyn, Great Outdoors Publishing Co.

FISHING, Gil Paust, Sterling Books.

FISHING IN PACIFIC WATERS, J. C. Davis, Sentinel Books.

FISHING ON THE FLORIDA KEYS, Charles Mayott, Great Outdoors Publishing Co.

FISHING TACKLE AND GEAR, Don Shiner, Collier Books.

FRESH AND SALT WATER FISHING, Ray Ovington, Cornerstone Library.

FRESH WATER FISHES, Collier Books.

FRESH WATER FISHING, Ed Moore, Collier Books.

FRESH-WATER FISHING METHODS, Fisherman's Encyclopedia Staff, Collier Books.

HOW TO MAKE CLOTHESPIN LURES, Lawrence L. Snow, Great Outdoors Publishing Co.

HOW TO TAKE FRESH WATER FISH IN LAKE, POND, AND STREAM, Maurice H. Decker, Sentinel Books.

OUTDOOR LIFE FISHING BOOK, P. Allen Parsons, Grosset & Dunlap.

SALT-WATER FISHING METHODS, Fisherman's Encyclopedia Staff, Collier Books.

SALT WATER GAME FISHES, Fisherman's Encyclopedia Staff, Collier Books.

SPORTSMAN'S DIGEST OF FISHING, Hal Sharp, Barnes & Noble.

TROUT FISHERMAN'S BIBLE, Dan Holland, Doubleday.

Fishing Books (Hardcover)

THE NEW FISHERMAN'S ENCYCLOPEDIA, Ira N. Gabrielson Editor, Stackpole Books.

FISHING FLIES AND FLY TYING, William F. Blades, Stackpole Books.

HOW TO FISH FROM TOP TO BOTTOM, Sid Gordon, Stackpole Books.

MAN AGAINST MUSKY, Howard Levy, Stackpole Books.

FISHING SECRETS OF THE EXPERTS, Vlad Evanoff, Doubleday.

SALT WATER FISHING, Ban Campen Heilner, National Wildlife Book Service.

FISHING FOR FUN, Herbert Hoover, Random House.

WITH FLY, PLUG AND BAIT, Ray Bergman, Morrow Co.

FRESH WATER BASS, Ray Bergman, National Wildlife Book Service.

JUST FISHING, Ray Bergman, Alfred Knopf.

TROUT, Ray Bergman, National Wildlife Book Service.

THE FISH IN MY LIFE, Murray Hoyt, Crown Publications.

JAYBIRDS GO TO HELL ON FRIDAY, Havilah Babcock, Holt, Rinehart & Winston.

COMPLEAT ANGLER, Izaak Walton, Dutton, Nelson or Peter Pauper Press.

13

Should You Become a Sportswoman?

◈

◈

◈

There are two sides to every question, they tell us. But here is a question that has four sides, two male and two female. The following reactions from a pair of sportsmen will give you an idea of the conflicting masculine opinions:

Pro. "This year five times as many wives may be expected to hunt with their husbands as did in 1955; three times as many wives as in 1960! . . . And those ladies who don't go in for outdoor activities with their husbands are missing something they'd better look into quick."

Con. "We are up against something basic. Most of the

avid hunters and fishermen do not care to have anchors around their necks. They want to go where they please and when they please; and once there, they want to indulge in hard hunting or fishing and not serve in the capacity of guides. Furthermore, most wives detest black flies and snakes and would not like to be caught dead in a primitive place, where hunting and fishing is at its best."

Well, there you are. You toss a coin and you take your choice. Or do you? What about the woman's angle?

The reports from women are various. If the husband wants to hunt or fish alone, and his wife doesn't care to join him—fine! If the man likes wifely company on his sporting jaunts, and his wife enjoys the outdoors with him —fine again! One kind of difficulty comes when the man thinks his wife doesn't love him if she won't endure "black flies and snakes" with him. Another results when the wife wants to be a good sport and get into the outdoorsman's act, and he'd like to be left alone.

The best advice I can give is, don't consider becoming a sportswoman unless these two conditions are both firmly met: (1) Your husband sincerely encourages you to do so, and (2) you have a strong personal interest in hunting and/or fishing.

ARE YOU THE HUNT-AND-FISH TYPE?

The proponents of women in outdoor sports remind us of women's long history as hunters, and the worship of Diana, goddess of the hunt, by the ancient Greeks and Romans. They remind us of the legendary Amazons, recently reported to be living yet in the heart of the Peruvian jungle in South America. These giant women continue to hunt with the men and are skillful with the bow and arrow. Whether they still amputate their right breasts to facilitate the use of weapons has not been determined, as nobody dares get close enough to such people to investigate.

"Women hunters have traditionally been good shots," says a press release from the National Shooting Sports Foundation. Maybe so, but I don't see any women's names in the record books of the Olympic and Pan-American Games. They are occasionally reported making record fishing catches, and we find that Jane Haywood made such a catch at LaPaz, Mexico, in 1963, a 52-pound-6-ounce snook; and Mrs. Earl Small once caught a champion 4-pound-12-ounce perch at Messalonskee Lake, Maine; Mrs. Lee Hallberg caught a whopper of a 31-pound silver salmon earlier at Cowichan Bay, British Columbia.

The sports magazines and newspaper sports columns often encourage the aspiring Diana with stories of the prowess of women in catching big game. We read of a Mrs. Clive Stolks of Basin, Wyoming ("Wood, Field, and Stream," Oscar Godbout, *New York Times*) who shot an 800-pound cow moose at a hundred and fifty feet and got him "cleanly behind the ear." We find a story by Adeline E. Hollemon (*Outdoor Life*, April, 1964), in which she says, "I stalked and killed my first antelope twenty years ago. My husband, who formerly lived in the foothills of the Colorado Rockies, and I have hunted for twenty-seven of the twenty-eight years we have shared together. Part of my childhood was spent trailing my brother when he hunted cougars in the hills bordering our farm near Alsea, Oregon." Her latest triumph—a pronghorn antelope that a male hunter pursued in vain for five days.

Should You Become a Sportswoman?

Robert C. Ruark tells the tale *(Field and Stream,* November, 1961) of a lady, Darlene Robinson, who just went along for the ride on her husband's safari but was determined to have a leopardskin rug as a memento. She got her game in the more traditionally feminine way. She just kept prodding her husband, so that in the end I suppose it was easier to catch the elusive leopard than put up with her taunts.

Whether you are an active or passive participant in your outdoorsman's hobby, the fashion stylists have something for you. I don't know whether Oleg Cassini or the House of Dior is ready to design anything of practical use for field and stream, but they've been calling many of their informal styles "sportive," which shows a trend.

Now that there are a million licensed women hunters and seven million women who fish for sport, the American clothes manufacturer is catering to them with coats and blouses that have shoulder recoil padding, and with slacks and skirts with "paratroop" pockets for shotgun shells. You can also get kilts with a sporran-type cartridge-holder.

There are all kinds of "his and her" outfits available for hunting and fishing. One set, for cool weather, could double as a skating or skiing ensemble. It is made of heavy cotton duck, bonded to Scott foam, and is water-repellent. The sleeves and trousers are bordered with knit cuffs to fit snuggly, and there is a matching pile-lined hood. The women's model comes in hunter's red, camel tan, or (gun?)powder blue, the men's in hunter's red or antelope brown.

Another, lighter weight set for fishing is made of nylon

fabric rubberized on the inside, with drawstring hood and drawstring waist on the pants. A third is made for hunting, of dacron polyester and cotton poplin, and consists of a hunter's coat and pants in tan color. The jacket has a corduroy collar and a bellowed game pocket that snaps back when empty. Matching hunter's caps are also procurable.

With any of these, a woman can wear a pair of women's boots or a variety of the men's waterproof, insulated pac designed for boys and women.

There are many lightweight shotguns of six to seven pounds, and some rifles weigh only five pounds, so that a woman doesn't need to feel too encumbered when carrying a gun. Most guns also have built-in rubber recoil pads to save fragile shoulders from bruising.

As for fishing equipment, it is notably light in weight and easy to manage. The only fishing requiring extraordinary strength is big game fishing.

You can see that if you want to join your husband and be a sportswoman, the manufacturers of equipment are quite ready to oblige. Recreational and shooting facilities throughout the nation are also said to welcome the attendance of women. According to the National Shooting Sports Foundation, "women tend to lend greater amiability to the sport of hunting and shooting." I don't know exactly what they mean by that, but apparently they feel the feminine presence adds some important elements.

Well, what about it? Do you want to join the one million women who hunt big and small game and waterfowl? Or the seven million who engage in fresh- and salt-water fishing? If you do, more power to you! (But check this once more with your husband, just to be really sure!)

It has been suggested that gun shops, sporting equipment departments, and the sports section of your local book store are ideal places for a single girl to meet men. So maybe you should encourage your daughter to take up one of the two sports. She can also meet men on the rifle range, at the hunting lodge, and out fishing. A girl interested in outdoor sports can become acquainted with more sportsmen, and thus have a wider choice of a healthy mate, than a girl who spends her vacations at resort hotels lying beside the pool all day and standing hopefully around the dance floor in the evening. As the saying goes, "If you want a sportsman, go where the sportsmen are!"

CAN YOU DIG UP AN OUTDOOR HOBBY?

Let's assume you don't care to become a sportswoman yourself. There are many other ways to share your husband's enjoyment of outdoor life. You can adopt nature hobbies of your own, like bird-watching, outdoor photography, or shell collection. Hunting and fishing are both seasonal hobbies to a great extent, so that your sportsman will have many week ends during the year in which you and he can share the outdoors together. Take up some nature hobby that the whole family can join you in, if you wish. Or just branch out on your own. When your husband has finished telling you about that trout he landed, or that deer he stalked, you can come back with that snow goose or egret or red-eyed vireo you caught in your binoculars. If photography is your bent, you can show him your shots of the local squirrels, rabbits, and chipmunks.

You can share a love of the shore with a surf-casting husband by collecting rare shells from among those that are washed up along its sands.

Birding is an easy nature hobby for anyone with a back yard. Just put up a feeder in winter or a few birdhouses in summer, and maybe a birdbath, and your feathered friends will show up to entertain you. If you live in an apartment in town, there is still plenty of opportunity to watch birds, and you will find them in the most unlikely spots. In Washington Square Park, oblivious of the beatniks and guitar-players, there are thrushes, towhees, flickers, thrashers, sapsuckers, and brown creepers. Out at the 1964-65 New York World's Fair, among the hustle and bustle of a hundred thousand people, I have seen a brown thrasher and a woodpecker making themselves at home in a pavilion garden. In the sculpture court in back of the Museum of Modern Art, I have discovered a pair of little brown wrens in the shrubbery behind a reclining nude. Of course, if you go to one of the larger parks or wildlife refuges, your opportunities for observation are limitless. Your only equipment need be a pair of binoculars and a bird book, for reference and identification—unless you care to take along a portable tape recorder to record the sounds of nature.

Women often shy clear of photography as a hobby, because there seems to be a clear-cut choice between using an old-fashioned box type and looking like an amateur, or getting mixed up with 35 millimeters and reflexes, light meters and exposure meters, and the many complicated settings for various distances and weather conditions. All this can be forgotten now, with the invention of the new automatic cameras, which are self-adjusting and require nothing of you but the choice of a subject and the push of a button. These come in inexpensive models for the beginner, and more costly numbers that you can consider buying when you have developed some expertise. It's also a good idea to start with the less expensive black-and-white film until you have learned not to cut off heads and feet, and how to compose artistically. All this comes with practice and experience. Once you have switched to color you'll be hooked, since there is nothing like it for outdoor photography to reproduce the blues of skies and sea, the greens of woods and grass, and the colors that your live subjects—either human or animal—may be wearing at the time.

Shell collection is a hobby shared by people of all ages and professions, from high school students to surgeons. Some collectors never go near the sea, but get all their specimens by buying and trading. This, it seems to me, takes half the fun out of it. It is much more exciting to go to the shore at low tide and come across some rarity all by yourself than to send away for it through the mail. There are shell clubs in a number of localities in the United States, especially New England, Florida, and California, where you can find others to share information about your common interest.

Shells are beautiful; a study of their construction is educational; and some of them are quite valuable. On the market, a Voluta bednalli can bring as high as a hundred dollars—and it is a small brown shell only about three inches long. Don't search your beaches for one, though, in the hope of quick riches. It comes from northern Australia. Closer to home you may find the large, pink king-conch in

South Atlantic waters, the cone-shaped fusinus colus on North Atlantic shores, and the spirally constructed chambered nautilus in the Southern Pacific. Any shore anywhere will produce attractive specimens of one kind or another. It is easiest to start with deserted shells, whose inhabitants have died or moved to new quarters. The dedicated collector, however, takes shells when the animals are alive to procure the most perfect specimens. You will need instruction on the preparation of these live shells when you reach that point, and it will be advisable to go to your library or paperback book store for information on the subject.

HOW ABOUT SWIMMING, RIDING, OR SKIING?

Riding, water sports, and winter sports will not only keep you and the whole family healthy and strong; they also give you a wonderful time out in the beauties of Nature, where little irritations and troubles get allocated to their right proportions.

As for water sports, everyone should know how to swim. In this country, in spite of the fact that our experts in water sports constantly win Olympic medals, one out of two Americans cannot swim. Learning to swim is a basic requirement for your own safety and welfare. After that, the choice is limitless and fascinating. All you need is an ocean, lake, or river. You can buy or rent a small two-man boat to go sailing, a motorboat to pull you along on water skis, or a scuba diving outfit to investigate the underwater depths. The simple purchase of a face mask, snorkel, and swim fins will equip you to try yourself out at skin diving in shallower water near the shore. No sports are better than these for figure and complexion—and for over-all relaxation.

Another exercise that takes you into the outdoors, but is neglected by many because they never happened to learn, is horseback riding. Have you ever seen women riding along a beach or bridle path, looking so fit and at the same time so aristocratic? With a little gumption, you can get out there and do the same thing. All it takes is a few lessons and the rental of a horse. Find someone else to take up the sport along with you, or someone who already has experience and can help you. You'll benefit in fitness, weight control (trotting uses up five hundred calories hourly), and philosophical outlook.

There has been a great upsurge in the popularity of winter sports in recent years. This is due to a number of factors: The publicity they receive when winter Olympics are broadcast on television; the effort of mountain summer resort areas to become winter resorts as well; the need of railroads and bus lines to build up winter week end travel; and the delight of the sports equipment and clothes manufacturers at the opportunity for new business.

All this has made skiing, in spite of broken arms and legs, the "in" thing to do. (Ice-skating has not received a similar build-up. Could it be because all the equipment required is a pair of skates, and you only need travel to the nearest pond or rink?) If photographs of those charmingly cozy ski lodges, with their wood beams and open fireplaces and ruggedly handsome skiers, haven't already entranced you, the illustrations of ski styles in your fashion pages certainly will. No longer do we have the baggy pants and thickly padded parkas of earlier years. Today there are stretch trousers, with long jackets that fit slinkily over the hips, made of quilted nylon taffeta, embroidered cotton poplin, or embossed DuPont nylon, and double-knit wool, all in smart black and white or colors.

Something that is great fun to take up is snowshoeing, which doesn't require mountain resorts, and can be practiced in your own neighborhood, without benefit of any special type of clothes. All you need is warm clothing and heavy socks and a pair of snowshoes. The whole family can go out and explore the white woods and fields together, and make a picnic of it, coming home at night to your own personal winter sport lodge, with or without fireplace.

We got into this subject because of your sportsman husband. But he's getting his outdoor experiences already, whether you join him or not. Your children, however, cannot be so independent. Every hour that you spend swimming, riding, hiking, skating, or skiing with them is a contribution to their health and fulfillment of personality.

◇
◇
◇
◇
◇
◇
◇
◇

14

You Can Be Happier with a Sportsman

◇

◇

◇

There are innumerable advantages to being married to a sportsman. (And with only another couple of pages left in the book, we should not—without the epigrammatic gift of Shakespeare—even begin to discuss such an awe-inspiring topic.) There are times when the garage is full of floating duck down; or the kitchen sink is populated by a listless fish that father and the children are attempting to revive after it's been in a boat for several hours. There are also times when the fishing party is eight hours overdue, and there's such a storm raging that even the local sky patrol can't go out searching. Those are our hours of temptation. Even so, there isn't any doubt at all that life with a sportsman brings you a load of blessings. Let's consider some—and we *are* going to generalize!

First. The instincts that impell a man to hunt and fish show that he is at heart a provider and protector of his family. The sportsman is usually a good family man, a reliable provider, and a strong help in emergency situations.

Second. The trips into the out-of-doors give a man a chance to wear rugged clothes, let his beard grow, use indiscreet language, and otherwise release his repressions. The sportsman therefore is usually a gentleman in civilized surroundings. Frequently the most rugged outdoorsman is the one you can most count on always to shave, dress neatly, and watch his language around women and children.

Third. Your outdoorsman gets physical exercise and communion with nature. He develops some idea of what it means to be a good sport and play fair. In this era of chronic fatigue (or apathy, or laziness, or whatever), he isn't too tired to lend a hand when you're worn out sometimes—and he does it like a man who loves you, not like a slave you've got wrapped around your finger.

Fourth. The sportsman likes nature, likes hunting, likes fishing—likes his buddies. He's not so apt to be a habitual complainer as a man who never gets out and spends days at a time doing what he really likes, with people he really likes.

Fifth. Sportsmen are often pretty funny people. The art of exaggeration is usually rather highly developed in them. Many of them are equally accomplished in the art of thinking up practical jokes—the very rough, woodsy type, like slipping a bucketful of brook trout into your sleeping bag and waking you up with shouts to swim for your life because you've slipped into the creek. (That type is particularly hilarious in cold weather.) This boyish, playful, humorous quality is great for the children, though, and helps make a man a good father.

Sixth. The sportsman isn't around your neck during all his spare time. According to the statistics, he gives you a week out of each year in which you are free to indulge yourself, amuse yourself, build yourself up, or let yourself go, as the mood takes you. When he is home, the hunter and fisherman is never bored. He is polishing up his gear, practicing marksmanship, tying flies, reading sports literature, or engaging in various do-it-yourself sporting projects. Never being bored himself, he is seldom a bore to others.

Seventh. The sportsman brings home table delicacies that you would have to travel all over the world to have served to you in a restaurant. He helps (and sometimes joins) his wife in becoming a gourmet cook.

Eighth. The outdoorsman, by paying taxes and using his influence, preserves many millions of acres of our country in all its natural beauty. The land he saves for his recreation can also be used for yours and your children's.

Ninth. The sportsman supports the American economy with his purchase of clothing and equipment from a billion dollar industry that is constantly expanding. He helps make the economy prosperous, and a prosperous country is a place where wives are well-fed, well-dressed, and generally pampered.

Tenth. The hunter and fisherman is so darned happy to get home from roughing it out in the woods, in spite of his profession of enjoying all the hardships along with the rewards, that he appreciates his wife and the comforts she provides twice as much. A sportsman may like the outdoors, but he loves his wife and home.

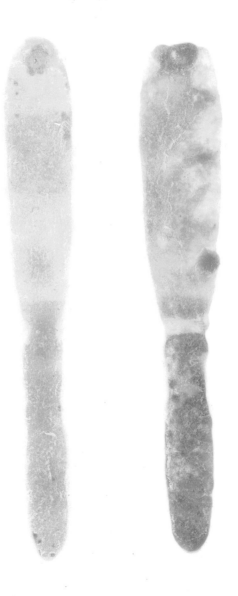

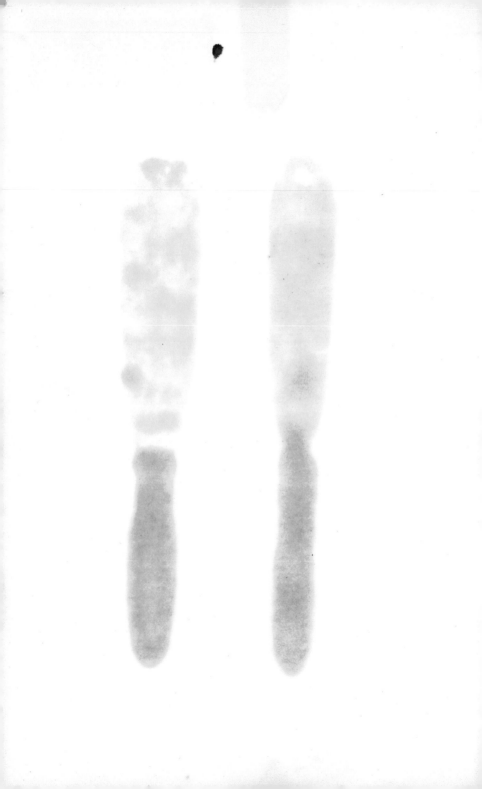

MAX and ME and the
and the
TIME MACHINE

MAX and ME and the TIME MACHINE

by Gery Greer and Bob Ruddick

Harcourt Brace Jovanovich, Publishers

San Diego   New York   London

Requests for permission to make copies of any part of the work should
be mailed to: Permissions, Harcourt Brace Jovanovich, Publishers,
757 Third Avenue, New York, New York 10017.

Library of Congress Cataloging in Publication Data
Greer, Gery.
Max and me and the time machine.
Summary: Steve buys a time machine at a garage sale
and takes his friend Max to the year 1250, where they
land in the middle of a jousting match, with the fierce
Sir Bevis as an enemy.
[1. Space and time—Fiction. 2. Middle Ages—Fiction.
3. Knights and knighthood—Fiction] I. Ruddick, Bob.
II. Title.
PZ7.G85347Max 1983   [Fic]   82-48762
ISBN 0-15-253134-3

Designed by Vaughn Andrews
Printed in the United States of America
First edition   B C D E

To Barbara and Scott

and to

Geraldine Greer and C. K. Ruddick

MAX and ME and the TIME MACHINE

1

I guess I'm like everybody else. When I do something that's pretty terrific, I expect to get some credit for it. A little praise, a pat on the back, a bit of wild, thunderous applause—maybe even a chorus of "Bravo! Fantastic! Way to go!"

And that's just what I was expecting when I hauled that huge crate into our clubhouse and told my best friend, Max Zilinski, that it contained a time machine I had picked up at a garage sale down the street. For $2.50.

But Max did not applaud. He snorted.

"Who're you trying to kid, Steve?" he said, barely glancing up from the electronics book he was reading. "There's no such thing as time travel. *Or* time machines."

I wiped the sweat off my forehead with the back of my sleeve and slouched against the crate. "When have I ever lied to you?" I asked, trying to look hurt and sincere at the same time.

"An interesting question," said Max, carefully laying his book aside on the rumpled cot and holding up his fingers to count on. "Now, let me see. I can recall the Rotten Toboggan Affair . . ."

Uh-oh, here we go. Max has all these code names for the various little misunderstandings we've had. The Rotten Toboggan Affair referred to that day last winter when I talked him into going down Quarter-Mile Hill on a beat-up old toboggan. "You're crazy," Max had said. "This hill is too steep and this toboggan is a mess. Look at it. It's even rotting out underneath."

It took a lot of doing, but I finally convinced him that the toboggan was as good as new and as sound as a rock. A couple of minutes later, as we were tearing down the hill at about eighty miles an hour, the toboggan began to come apart. Little pieces began breaking off, and we lost control, hit a tree stump, somersaulted through the air, and smashed into a snowbank. Max remembers things like that.

". . . and the Taste-Tempting Tip . . ."

Was it my fault that liver-and-kidney-flavored Puppy Chewies taste worse, not better, than they look?

". . . and let's not forget Operation Lousy Letter!"

See what happens when you try to help a friend? I mean, could I have known that Max, who is always trying to work up the nerve to talk to Dawn Sharington, would get upset when I broke the ice by writing her a love letter and signing his name to it?

"Okay, okay," I said, holding up my hands in surrender. "Let's not quibble over a few minor mistakes. After all, what do you care if Dawn knows you think she's the best-looking girl west of the Mississippi?"

Max made a choking sound.

"Besides, you should thank me. You wanted

Dawn to notice you, and now she does. Whenever she sees you, she starts giggling like crazy."

"Agggggggggh," groaned Max, clutching his head with both hands.

"Look, Max," I said cheerfully, "forget about the letter. We've got something a lot more important to deal with. I mean, haven't we been wondering for the last two weeks what we were going to do all summer? Well, now we've got the answer."

I patted the time-machine crate meaningfully and read the black lettering stamped on the side: MAINLY, ONE GENUINE, COMPLETELY AUTOMATED, EASILY ASSEMBLED, ONE-OF-A-KIND TIME MACHINE! FULLY GUARANTEED!

"Sure, sure," grumbled Max. "And you got it at a garage sale for two fifty. You don't expect me to believe that, do you?"

"If you'll just listen a minute," I said, "I can explain the whole thing. Okay?"

Max grunted, but he was still suffering over Dawn. This sales pitch was going to have to be good.

"Okay. You know Mr. Cooper, right? The man who lives just around the corner in that great big old house? Well, he found this crate in his attic last night, and he's sure it was left there by the famous Professor Flybender."

Max's logical mind slowly clicked into gear. "Oh, yeah? If this professor guy is so famous, how come I've lived here in Flat Rock for five years and never heard of him? And why would he leave things in Mr. Cooper's attic?"

"Good points. I asked Mr. Cooper the same

3

things. It turns out that Flybender used to live there and was some sort of crazy inventor. You know, setting off explosions in his basement and racing around on his roof during thunderstorms. About eight years ago, he announced that he was off to find the lost continent of Atlantis, and nobody has seen him since. Eventually, the house was sold to pay off the professor's debts, and Mr. Cooper bought it."

"Okay, Sherlock, then why didn't Mr. Cooper find this marvelous invention before now?" Max smugly pushed his glasses back up on his nose.

"Because, Watson, there was so much junk in the attic when Mr. Cooper bought the house he never had time to go through it all. But this morning he was looking for stuff to put on sale, and that's when he spotted the crate. He dragged it down and put it out with a bunch of chipped dishes and old clothes."

"I still say you've been had," Max insisted stubbornly. "If Mr. Cooper actually believed this was a time machine, do you really think he would have sold it to you?"

"Of course not," I scoffed. I was ready for that one, too. "But just because Mr. Cooper is too short-sighted to recognize a great discovery like this doesn't mean we have to be, too. After all, you're the one who's always telling me that scientific geniuses are misunderstood in their own times."

Max seemed impressed with this argument, since it was one of his own. Nibbling his thumbnail thoughtfully, he got up and began to circle the crate slowly.

"Well, just for the sake of argument," he said, "let's *suppose* this Professor Flybender really was a brilliant inventor, and *suppose* he really did build this thing, and *suppose* he really did leave it in Mr. Cooper's attic . . ."

Max's voice trailed off as he mulled over his supposes.

Max is like that. He *thinks* about everything, weighing all the angles, considering all the options. Maybe it comes from being a compulsive reader. I mean, Max goes for books like a hungry piranha goes for toes, which means he knows *something* about almost everything. It also means his brain works overtime. I call him Motor-Mind.

As for me, I prefer action. It saves time. I can eat two ice-cream cones in the time it takes Max to consider the relative merits of vanilla versus peanut-pumpkin swirl.

And I could see it was time to act. I thumped the crate loudly with the flat of my hand—THUMP.

"Max, my boy, this is Opportunity Knocking." THUMP, THUMP. "Think of it—a *time machine*! A hot rod into history! Why, with this baby we could go anywhere we want—to any *time* we want. Just consider the possibilities!"

THUMP! "We could travel back three thousand years to ancient Egypt and catch the grave robbers as they jimmy their way into King Tut's tomb!"

Max's eyes glazed slightly as he considered that possibility.

THUMP! "We could ride with Attila the Hun and his mighty hordes as they terrorize the Roman Empire!"

"Yeah," whispered Max in an awed voice. "And if

5

we stopped off in the seventeenth century, I could get Shakespeare's autograph!"

He was hooked. Of course, I had no intention of chasing around through time trying to get some guy's autograph, but we could iron out that detail later.

I hopped up onto a stool. "We could drop in on the nineteenth century and solve the Jack the Ripper murders!"

"Wow!" said Max, joining in. "And attend the opening night of Beethoven's Fifth Symphony!"

I jabbed my finger at the ceiling and cried, "Babe Ruth, Billy the Kid, Blackbeard the Pirate!"

"Aristotle, Galileo, Einstein!" Max shouted.

I made a flying leap onto the table, threw back my head, and yelled, "The Gunfight at the O.K. Corral!"

Max was overcome. He snapped to attention and saluted up at me. "Say no more, chief," he said, his face glowing with enthusiasm. "Just tell me what you want me to do."

I jumped down and held out my hand. "Fork over two dollars," I said. "I was a little short of the asking price, and Mr. Cooper said he'd take the time machine back if I didn't come up with the rest of the money before eleven o'clock."

2

Putting the time machine together was a cinch. We just followed the step-by-step instructions in the professor's booklet on ASSEMBLING FLYBENDER'S FANTASTIC, FULLY GUARANTEED TIME MACHINE. Nobody bothered us either, which is one of the big advantages of having a clubhouse of our own. We'd built it ourselves out in my backyard, where it's almost completely hidden by trees. Even my nosy little sister usually leaves us alone.

By one o'clock, the time machine was finished. As we shook hands and stood back to admire our work, the weird seven-foot-tall contraption seemed to be staring down at us.

"We may have just assembled Flybender's Fantastic Hunk of Junk," commented Max, eyeing the machine doubtfully. "Does this thing look like a time machine to you?"

"You bet," I lied. "And what a beaut."

Actually, Max had a point. It did look sort of like a hunk of junk. In fact, with all the confusion of dials and meters and switches and colored lights, and that ridiculously tiny map of the world pinned under glass, and that enormous ON-OFF lever jutting out from the side, the machine could have been anything. Mostly, it looked like a giant jelly-bean dispenser from outer space.

As for the inner workings, they were a complete mystery, because most of the work we'd done was limited to screwing knobs and glass plates and other loose parts onto the outer surface of the machine. Like, for instance, the overgrown fan that, following the professor's instructions, we had bolted on top. I had the uneasy feeling that if we turned that fan on, it would turn the clubhouse inside out.

All in all, it was hard to believe Flybender's machine could transport anybody anywhere—especially through time. But I wasn't going to waste time worrying about it. I believe in positive thinking.

While I cleaned up, Max fine tuned the controls, checking the instruction manual to see that the meters were calibrated, the switches were in the correct positions, and all buttons had been pushed in the proper sequence.

I guess you'd say that next to reading, Max's favorite pastime is tinkering with mechanical gadgets. He even put together a pretty impressive robot once, named Big Ed. Last summer we smuggled it up to Camp Wongahana and into a closet in our group's cabin. Then, when all the lights were out, and right in the middle of one of Sid Berman's hair-raising ghost stories, Max pushed a button on his hand-held, remote-control unit, and Big Ed came slamming out of the closet door. His face glowed like a ghoul's, and he made a horrible gurgling noise. Of course, if Sid hadn't been telling ghost stories at the time, everybody probably wouldn't have panicked the way they did, and our counselor wouldn't have led that stampede out of the cabin, screaming, "It's the Un-dead! It's the Un-dead!"

So Max couldn't take *all* the credit for how he and I and Big Ed had the whole cabin to ourselves for the next couple of hours.

Still, he does have a way with machines.

"That's it," said Max, snapping the manual shut. "According to the professor, all we have to do now is select a time and place we want to visit. When our time is up, we'll be automatically returned to the present. And no matter how long we're gone, no time will have passed here, so no one will even know we've been away."

"You mean we'll come back exactly when we left?" I asked.

"That's what the manual says," said Max.

"Great!" I said, pacing the floor with excitement. "And of course since I found the time machine, I get to choose where we go on our first trip. And I choose the Middle Ages."

"The Middle Ages?" said Max, with a puzzled frown. "What's so great about the Middle Ages?"

I slapped my forehead in disgust. "Have you been asleep for the last thirteen years, or what? Haven't you ever heard of knights in shining armor? Haven't you heard of castles and dungeons and damsels in distress? Wouldn't you like a little Action, Adventure, and Excitement?"

"No," said Max.

"I can see it now," I continued, striking a gallant pose. "There we'd be, galloping over the green hills and through the dark forests, rescuing fair maidens who are in danger up to their armpits."

Max snorted. "Everyone knows that all that stuff about rescuing damsels in distress is just a bunch of bunk."

"Oh, yeah? I don't suppose you've ever thought about how it'd be to rescue Dawn Sharington from distress."

Max blushed. "Well," he grumbled, quickly changing the topic, "if we're going to the Middle Ages, we're going to have to nail down the exact date. How does 1250 A.D. sound? That would put us right in the middle of the best century of the whole Middle Ages."

"Whatever you say," I agreed. "You're the history expert."

Max bent toward the control panel of the time machine, squinting. I peered over his shoulder. All the controls were preset except for the three in the center of the panel, outlined with a ring of colored lights. The first was marked "Dial-a-Date." By turning the knobs under the window, you could dial any date you wanted. Max carefully dialed A.D. 1250.

The second control, "Pick-a-Place," had a tiny world map under glass. Max fiddled with the knobs and found that they moved a red dot across the face of the map, marking the place you wanted to be transported to.

"Might as well make it jolly old England," he said, jockeying the red dot into position.

I couldn't believe it—a trip to medieval England!

My skin prickled, and I began to beat out a drum roll on the table.

"As for our 'Length-of-Stay,' " continued Max briskly as he examined the third control, "since this is a trial run, I say we drop in for about three hours."

"*Three hours!*" The drums stopped in midroll. "*Three hours!* What can we do in three measly little hours?"

"We can stay out of trouble, that's what." Max squared his shoulders and crossed his arms over his chest. "Take it or leave it. I'm crazy enough just letting you talk me into trying this thing in the first place."

He meant it.

"You win," I sighed.

With a satisfied nod, Max turned to adjust the "Length-of-Stay" controls. He set the numbers knobs to read "003" and then spun the units knob past "Years" and "Days" to lock in on "Hours." Three hours. Big deal. Baseball games can last longer than that.

I was disappointed, and I guess that's why I did it. I know I shouldn't have, but when Max took his glasses off to polish them on his shirt tail, I reached over and moved the last numbers knob forward five notches. What could it hurt if we were in the Middle Ages for eight hours instead of three?

To cover myself, I kept an eye on Max and observed loudly, "Do you realize what this means? We're actually going to travel through time! You and me. Steve Brandon and Maximilian Zilinski."

"Yeah." Max's voice wavered, as if he weren't too sure he really liked the idea. "Maybe we should gather up some supplies or sandwiches or something and go tomorrow morning. What do you think?"

I hate waiting. Besides, waiting might give Max time to change his mind.

"There's no time like the present," I said.

"Then why are we going to the Middle Ages?" said Max dryly.

He put his glasses back on and started for the door. "Anyway," he added, "why don't we go over to my house and have something to eat? My mother can make us one of her famous avocado-and-chili sandwiches, and we can talk the whole thing over."

I figured it was now or never.

Almost without thinking, I reached out, grasped the huge ON-OFF lever, and by throwing my full weight against it, pulled it down to "ON." Max spun around, but there was nothing he could do. He was clear across the room, with his hand on the doorknob and one foot out the door. I barely had time to glimpse his startled expression before Professor Flybender's Fully Guaranteed Time Machine sprang to life.

3

Lights flashed, gauges gyrated, steam spewed out of loose joints with the force of a fire hose turned on full blast.

Flybender's machine was working, all right.

Then, from deep inside, came a weird, wild, wailing sound. It was low like a moan but rose steadily until it reached an eerie high pitch. And at that moment the giant fan on top of the machine began to spin, ghostly slow at first, but gaining speed . . . faster . . . faster . . .

The clubhouse began to vibrate . . . faster. . . . I was thrown up hard against the shaking walls . . . faster. . . . Max began to look fuzzy around the edges . . . faster. . . . Now he was a blur . . . faster. . . .

"*Max!*" I shouted. And was immediately plunged into darkness.

The wind whistled by in furious whirlwinds, howling around my head and pulling at my hair. I felt as if I were on a vibrating conveyor belt, out of control and hurtling through a long ink-black tunnel.

A panicky feeling welled up inside me. I pushed it

down and tried to call out to Max, but the wind caught his name and swept it away.

Where was Max? Why was this taking so long? Why weren't we in the Middle Ages? Why—

Without warning, the vibrating stopped, and I fell several feet, landing with a heavy thud.

It was all over, but where was I? There were no lights, no sounds.

Blinking into the blackness, I tried to look around, but for some reason I couldn't move my neck. I tried to stand up but discovered that I couldn't move my legs. I tried a dog-paddle, but it was no go. *I was pinned.*

Now what? I wondered grimly.

Suddenly, I was startled by a strange, clinky-jingling noise and the uncomfortable feeling that I was turning, like a chicken on a barbecue spit, slowl-l-l-l-ly in space.

A narrow slit of light appeared in front of my eyes.

Then, into that slit of light popped a face—round, eager, about sixteen years old, with brown bobbed hair. He examined me with concern for a few moments before asking anxiously, "Art thou all right, Sir Robert?"

Before I could answer, the round-faced stranger pulled me to a sitting position and lifted a massive, flat-topped helmet off my head. I gaped down at myself in amazement.

No wonder I made a clinking noise whenever I moved. My T-shirt, jeans, and tennis shoes were gone. In their place was a long chain-mail shirt that covered me from head to knee, and underneath that, a pair of chain-mail tights. Over the armor, I was sporting a sleeveless, emerald-green tunic with a coat of arms embroidered in gold across my chest. And from my belt hung a long sword in a gold scabbard.

But even more amazing, I was wearing *someone else's body*! Someone tall and broad-shouldered, with plenty of well-developed muscles.

Not bad, I thought to myself, as I flexed my arm and felt the muscles ripple.

"Art thou all right, Sir Robert?" repeated the stranger. He was wearing a simple brown tunic over green tights, and soft leather boots with pointed toes.

"I sure art," I said cheerfully. As I spoke, I noticed that even my voice was different. It was deeper than my own, and stronger too. "But if you don't mind my asking, who art you?"

"Why, I am Niles, Sir Robert. Thy squire. Dost thou not know me?" He shook his head and looked worried. "Thou hast taken a nasty tumble off thy horse, and methinks it hath rattled thy wits."

He was wrong there. My wits were in tip-top condition. In fact, you might say that my wits were doing handsprings for joy as I realized several things:

- Flybender's machine had worked after all, and I was in the Middle Ages as planned.
- I had been transported into the body of a Sir Robert, a knight, and this guy, Niles, was his squire.
- As I entered Sir Robert's body, I must have gotten dizzy and fallen off my horse, which explained why Niles thought my wits were rattled, and why I had arrived with my nose in the dirt.

15

Then it hit me. If I came back in someone else's body, Max could be here, too, and I'd never recognize him. I began to look around with serious interest.

I was on a grassy field, surrounded by a makeshift camp of large, brightly colored tents, each decorated with flags and pennants that fluttered in the breeze. Looming a short distance to the right were the gray stone walls and turrets of a medieval castle. And by my side stood a sleek white horse draped with yards and yards of green cloth trimmed in gold.

Here and there men and boys scurried, all dressed like Niles in tunics and tights. Max could be anywhere, even miles from here.

I realized that if I were ever going to find him, I'd need a lot more information. And as Niles helped me to my feet, I thought of a plan to get it.

I shook my head as if I were still dazed. "Niles," I said, hoping I looked lost and confused, "I can't seem to get my bearings. I'm afraid that falling off my horse has made me lose my memory. Maybe if you'd tell me where we are and what we're doing here, it will all come back to me."

It worked. Niles looked up at me anxiously, with loyal devotion written all over his face. "Why, Sir Robert, we are at the Great Hampshire Tournament, where we have camped these past three days in thy tent." He gestured to the yellow-gold tent with green banners that stood behind us. "We came at the invitation of Richard Lorraine, Earl of Hampshire, who heard tales of thy great strength and skill at jousting and would try thee against his own champion. 'Tis the last day of the tourney, and thou art undefeated as usual, sire. Eighteen knights have fallen already before thy lance. There remaineth only the joust with Sir Bevis, a minor feat for someone with thy mighty talents."

I nodded cautiously. "I see. And just when is this minor jousting match supposed to take place?"

"In but a few moments, Sir Robert," he said, busily dusting off my tunic and straightening my belt. "Then the tourney will be over, and thou wilt be the champion. The people await this last joust most eagerly."

"Hmmmm. And you think I can handle Sir Bevis, do you?"

Niles laughed merrily. "Oh, Sir Robert, thou art jesting, of course. 'Twill be a sad day for English knighthood when thou, the Green Falcon, canst not best the likes of Sir Bevis."

Bingo! Jackpot! Things were looking good. Not only was I in the Middle Ages, but I was in the body of a famous knight and was actually going to be in a jousting match on the field of honor! And it was my kind of contest—me against some harmless, lily-livered, mealy-mouthed twerp.

The only problem was that it all sounded a bit beneath my talents. Why then, I wondered, were the people so eager to see this particular match? I decided to fish for a few details.

"Tell me, Niles," I said, cracking my knuckles and flexing my muscles, "who is this Bevis turkey anyway?"

"Why, Sir Bevis Thorkell," replied Niles cheerfully, "the Earl's champion and a knight known throughout all England as the Hampshire Mauler."

"The Hampshire *Mauler*?" I didn't like the sound of that.

"Aye, Sir Robert, and a black-hearted varlet he is. Canst thou truly remember nothing? Dost thou not recall his vow to smash thy skull and feed thy guts to the castle dogs, the saucy fellow?"

Saucy fellow? This was his idea of a saucy fellow? Something began to tell me I might not be cut out for the field of honor after all.

Niles continued gleefully. "Ho, ho! But I did put Sir Bevis in his place. Not two hours ago I met the knave within the castle walls. 'Is thy master ready to meet his doom?' he did ask me. 'Best thou lookest to thine own health,' I replied. 'Sir Robert will this very afternoon whack thee from thy horse, pommel and pound thee, and smite thee to smithereens.' "

"Gee," I said, laughing nervously. "I hope he didn't take that the wrong way."

Niles nodded happily. "That blow to thy head hath not robbed thee of thy sense of humor, Sir Robert." He chuckled contentedly to himself.

I found myself wondering if Sir Bevis and I could talk this thing over. I mean, I didn't want to be a spoilsport or anything, but let's face it, I don't perform well under pressure.

"Niles," I said, looking for an out, "give it to me straight. What has Sir Bevis got against me?"

" 'Tis no secret, sire. Sir Bevis is sore jealous that thou art a knight and are but eighteen years of age. He himself was not knighted until his twenty-first year, as is the common custom. And 'tis well known that the Earl hath taken a liking to thee during the tournament.

Mayhap Sir Bevis feareth that thou wilt replace him as the Earl's champion."

Niles blushed slightly. "And, of course, there is the matter of Lady Elizabeth."

"Oh?" I asked suspiciously. "What matter would that be?"

Niles's blush deepened and he looked away, embarrassed. "Ah, well, since thou hast lost thy memory, Sir Robert, I suppose I must admit that even I have noticed the glances that have passed between thyself and the Earl's fair daughter. And since Sir Bevis hopeth to make the Lady his wife, this hath only angered him the more."

"Okay," I said, shifting my weight uneasily. "Let me get this straight. Sir Bevis is a little upset because he thinks I'm trying to steal his reputation, his job, and his girl. Right?"

"Aye. And thou art just the man to do it."

"But—"

Suddenly, there was a loud blast of trumpets from somewhere nearby.

"Make haste, sire!" gasped Niles. " 'Tis time!"

Before I could say another word, he clapped the iron helmet back onto my head. A page ran out of a nearby tent, carrying some portable stairs which he plunked down next to the white stallion. I was still confused and stunned as Niles hustled me up the stairs and onto the horse, thrusting a shield into my left hand and a ten-foot-long lance into my right.

With a hearty "Go to, Sir Robert!" he slapped the horse's backside, and off we trotted in the direction of the trumpets.

"Where is Max now that I need him?" I groaned.

"Right here," said a deep voice from under me. "And you have my full support!"

It was Max! He was my horse!

"I heard everything Niles said," he continued with a whinny, "and I think it's safe to say that we're about to experience a little Action, Adventure, and Excitement."

With that, Max snorted noisily and pranced out onto the field of honor, proudly tossing his mane and humming the Notre Dame fight song, while I struggled wildly to hold my lance upright and stay in the saddle.

4

Lining one side of the large open field were long wooden bleachers crowded with cheering spectators. Women waved their scarves and handkerchiefs. Men stood and shouted. From the tops of tall poles, colored banners streamed and flapped in the breeze. On a raised platform behind the bleachers, twenty heralds snapped to attention, pressed golden trumpets to their lips, and blared out a rousing call to arms.

Little League was never like this.

Max tossed his head toward a lone figure mounted on a black steed at the opposite end of the field. "That must be Sir Bevis," he neighed.

It was the Hampshire Mauler, all right, and he looked ready to maul anything that got in his way. His chain mail, shield, sword, and helmet were coal black; and a blood-red tunic dripped from his massive shoulders. Even from a distance, he looked like a killer. I swallowed hard.

"Uh, look, Max," I stammered, "don't you think we should make a break for it before somebody around here gets hurt?"

21

"Relax," said Max, pawing the dirt eagerly. "I happen to know for a fact that jousting is more or less the safest of all the deadly dangerous sports in medieval England."

"Terrific," I said. "How silly of me to worry. I mean, what do I care about a ten-foot-long lance in the gut?"

Before Max could answer, the heralds blasted forth with another jarring fanfare. A hush fell over the crowd, and almost as a single body, they leaned forward in their seats. My heart took a nose dive down into where my tennis shoes should have been.

"Now what?" I hissed.

"No problem," whispered Max. "All you have to do is watch Sir Bevis and do whatever he does."

"Oh, sure," I said. "That's just great. And what if he runs me through with his lance?"

"In that case," said Max, "try not to land on your head. It'll only make matters worse."

I would have let him have it with my spurs, but I didn't have time. I caught some movement out of the corner of my eye, and I looked down the long field through the slits in my helmet. In the center were two narrow lanes separated by a low fence. And at the far end was Sir Bevis—evil, threatening, poised for the kill.

He lowered his lance until it was level and aimed steadily across the field straight at my heart.

What else could I do? I lowered my lance. It wobbled around like crazy.

Abruptly, the trumpets stopped, leaving the shock of silence. In that same instant, Sir Bevis spurred his black stallion and charged forward, his red tunic flapping and the tip of his lance glinting in the sun.

Without a word, Max too leaped forward. We were on a collision course with the Hampshire Mauler. The muffled thunder of hoofbeats filled the air. Hypnotized, I locked my eyes on the black figure bearing down on us. A cold fear gripped my spine, and I tried desperately to steady my lance.

He was almost upon us—so close that I thought I glimpsed his wild eyes gleaming evilly behind the slits in his black helmet. I braced myself for a terrible blow.

Suddenly, just before I was due to swallow the tip of Sir Bevis's lance, Max opened his mouth, curled back his lips, and at the top of his lungs bellowed: "GERONIMO-O-O-O-O-O-O-O-O-O-O-O-O-O-O-O-O!!!!!"

Sir Bevis's horse gave an alarmed squeal, dug all four hooves into the ground, and skidded to an abrupt halt.

Sir Bevis catapulted out of the saddle, sailed through the air, and fell with a noisy CLANK! onto the field. He was knocked out cold.

Child's play, I thought to myself as Max slowed to a stop and turned around. *This jousting business is mere child's play.*

The crowd went wild. And so they should. It was a brilliant performance.

Of course, from the bleachers, no one heard Max yell or saw that I had never laid a lance on Sir Bevis. All they knew was that on the very first pass, the Hampshire Mauler had been easily unhorsed and lay in a dazed heap on the field. And I was not about to spoil their fun by setting the record straight.

After all, it was the least I could do for Sir Robert while I was occupying his body. Being a hero, I mean. Keeping up the old boy's image in his absence. I'd do the same for anyone.

Max must have felt the same way, because he took plenty of time prancing past the stands, swishing his tail all over the place and snorting fiercely like some kind of wild Arabian stallion.

In the center of the stands was a special section covered with a fringed canopy. As we got closer, I could make out a stern-looking man with a rugged, sun-weathered face sitting under the canopy in a thronelike chair. Beside him was a strikingly pretty girl of about sixteen. She was blushing up a storm and had her eyes cast down at her lap, where she was twisting a long white scarf. Standing beside her, bobbing around gleefully, was a scrawny, gray-haired old woman, who waved us forward like a ground crewman bringing in a jumbo jet. She pointed a bony finger at the girl and winked at me.

Max whispered up at me out of the corner of his mouth. "That man is probably our host, the Earl of Hampshire. And you're in luck, Steve. That girl must be Lady Elizabeth."

"What do you mean, I'm in luck?" I hissed back.

Max didn't answer. Instead, he pulled up in front of the fringed box and, without any warning, bent his front legs and *bowed* before the Earl! The spectators gasped and applauded even more loudly. From everywhere came cries of "Sir Robert! Sir Robert! The Green Falcon!" Flowers flew through the air and fell at our feet. I guess they'd never seen a kneeling horse before.

Unfortunately, I had never been *on* a kneeling horse before. I was caught by surprise and was almost pitched out of the saddle. My lance swung down into the box, nearly nicking the Earl on the nose. He sat back cross-eyed with a startled grunt.

While I struggled to recover, Lady Elizabeth sprang forward and, with lightning speed, tied her white scarf onto the tip of my lance before I could regain my balance and pull it away. Then she fell back into her seat, smiling at me shyly and fluttering her eyelashes. I was glad I was still inside my helmet.

As Max stood up again, Niles suddenly appeared at our side, leading Sir Bevis's black stallion and carrying his black sword. I had read enough about the Middle Ages to know that when a knight wins a jousting match, he wins the other knight's armor and horse, although the loser usually buys back the loot. I guessed that Niles had taken Sir Bevis's sword and horse as a sort of token, since it wouldn't have been polite to strip him of his full armor while he was out cold on the field.

Niles put the sword down and untied Lady Elizabeth's scarf from my lance.

"Ahhhh," he exclaimed in a low voice, " 'twas a gesture of true love." Then, while my hands were full and I couldn't defend myself, he reached up and tucked the scarf inside my tunic—next to my heart. Lady Elizabeth giggled. The old woman skipped from foot to foot, chortling and rubbing her hands together with glee.

I was beginning to wish that Sir Bevis *had* run me through with his lance.

The Earl stood up to make a speech. He threw off his fur-lined cloak and stepped forward, holding up his hand as a signal for silence. The cheers died slowly away.

"Sir Robert Marshall," he boomed for all to hear, "never before have we seen such skill at arms as thou hast shown these past three days. Henceforth, let it be known throughout the land that thou wert the undefeated champion of the Hampshire Tournament in the year of our Lord, twelve hundred and fifty!"

Then, stroking his mustache, he added, "I would count it an honor, Sir Robert, if thou wouldst tarry a while as a guest here at Hampshire Castle. What sayest thou?"

Figuring that Sir Robert would want to accept, I cleared my throat and said, "I'd be happy to, your Earlship."

"Good, good," said the Earl. "Then thou wilt surely join us on the morrow for the hunt. We meet at dawn in the outer bailey."

Without waiting for a reply, he eased himself back into his chair, and the crowd immediately broke into a new storm of cheers and applause. So, while Niles led Sir Bevis's horse back to our tent, Max and I finished parading in front of the stands.

Even when we finally turned and headed back across the field, the thunder of applause followed us. It was great, but I felt a little sad when I realized that within a few short hours we'd be leaving the Middle Ages and winging our way back to our own time. We'd be trading tournaments for TV. It'd be good-bye to glory and hello to hanging around. I heaved a long sigh.

Max, on the other hand, was in high spirits.

"Hey, how about that Geronimo Gimmick?" he whinnied cheerfully. "Pretty terrific, don't you think? And I thought of it *joust* in time." He tittered at his own joke.

"Yeah," I sighed. "Terrific."

"But the best part was that Sir Bevis fell for it. Get it? *Fell* for it!"

"Oh, brother," I muttered, as Max gave a horsy guffaw and trotted briskly across the field toward Sir Robert's tent.

5

No doubt about it, I thought to myself as I entered Sir Robert's spacious, richly furnished tent, these medieval knights really know how to travel in style. As I scanned the elegant décor, I made mental notes so I could pass along a few pointers to our summer counselors at Camp Wongahana about the proper way to outfit a tent.

I noted with approval the thick carpet, the beautifully carved wooden trunks, the wide camp beds with fluffy quilts, the tasteful tapestries, the inviting leather chairs, and the strong oak table set with a slender flagon and several tall goblets made from stag horn and silver. And a squire to wait on me hand and foot—that was a nice touch.

"Sit thee here, Sir Robert," said Niles, bustling around in front of me and pulling a chair forward.

I sat down, and Niles carefully removed my helmet. He parted my hair and clucked over the nasty bump I'd gotten on my head when I fell off Max's back.

"Marry!" he exclaimed. " 'Tis little wonder that thou hast lost thy memory."

He smiled at me with open admiration. "Ah, Sir Robert, only a courageous knight such as thyself could fight such a rousing joust with an injury such as this. Thou art truly a man of iron."

This praise was met with a rude, snickering horse snort. I spun around, and there was Max, nosing his way into the tent.

Niles rushed forward, making shooing motions with his hands. "Out, out, thou sassy horse!" he cried.

Max wasn't impressed. He bared his teeth and snarled, flapping his lips for extra effect. Niles fell back with an astonished squeak.

"It's all right, Niles," I said, trying to keep the peace. "Let's let him in. He can't do any harm."

Niles sniffed primly. "Thou canst carry loyalty to thy horse too far, Sir Robert," he said.

"Says who?" muttered Max as he curled up on the rug.

But he didn't .mutter enough. Niles must have heard him because he froze, staring at Max bug-eyed. Then he shook his head hard, as if he were trying to dislodge a mosquito from his nose.

"Nay, nay, 'tis not possible," he mumbled to himself. "Methinks I have been too long in the sun these past three days."

He staggered over to one of the camp beds and collapsed weakly onto it.

Poor Niles. He really was a good-hearted guy. Kind, loyal, trustworthy—everything I always wanted in a squire.

I had just gotten up to find a wet cloth for his forehead, when a strange, chubby man in a long purple robe came dashing into the tent. Catching sight of me, he veered in my direction, tripped over the hem of his robe with both feet, and barely avoided a belly-flop by flailing out with his arm and hooking onto my shoulder.

He steadied himself and stared over at Niles, who had his hand on his head and was moaning, "The sun . . . too much sun . . ."

I figured I'd better say something.

"You must forgive Niles," I whispered. "He's been working too hard and . . . well . . . he's been imagining things. He actually thought he heard my horse talking!"

"Odd's bodkins!" declared the stranger, peeking around my shoulder at the squire. " 'Tis good fortune that I am a doctor. The lad needeth a dash of my pulverized fingernail clippings and a bit of bed rest."

"Oh, you're a *doctor*," I said, noticing for the first time the bulging red bag he was carrying. "Great. Maybe after you've taken care of Niles, you could look at this bump on my head."

" 'Twould be an honor, Sir Robert. But first, allow me to properly introduce myself." He carefully set down his red bag, puffed himself up like a purple balloon, and tossed his shoulder-length hair out of his eyes. "I am Clarence Gathergoods—Doctor, Alchemist, and Barber Extraordinaire."

He bowed gracefully, shoved me into a chair, and poked his finger at the wound on my head.

"Thou hast a bump here, all right," he said. He

fluffed my hair lightly. "And thou couldst use a trim around the sides, too."

Dr. Gathergoods beamed, seeming very pleased with himself for his speedy diagnosis. He patted his large paunch with satisfaction.

"Aye, aye," he declared. "Too much blood in the system. We shall have to bleed thee."

"*Bleed* me?" Was this guy a doctor or a vampire? Were we in England or Transylvania?

"Why, of course, Sir Robert. Everyone knoweth that in such cases blood-letting is the best cure."

He was wrong. I did not knoweth. If I had knoweth, I would have kept my big mouth shuteth about my bumpeth.

Dr. Gathergoods, however, was unconcerned. He hooked his thumbs in his gold belt and rocked back on his heels. "Just betwixt thee and me and the tent pole, Sir Robert, I am here at Hampshire Castle for a limited time only. I consider this quaint country castle to be but a temporary way station on my pilgrimage to greatness." His eyes glazed slightly. "Aye, 'tis but a matter of time before I shall unlock the secrets of alchemy and shall possess the power to transform ordinary metals to gold!"

He stood staring into space for a few moments and then shook himself out of his dreams and opened his bag. Peering inside, he fluttered his fingers in the air and fussed, "Now where are my leeches? I can never find *anything* in this bag."

Leeches? Whoa and wait a minute here, I thought. *This blood-letting business is bad enough, but leeches? No way. Count me out.*

I watched with a shudder as Dr. Gathergoods reached into his bag and drew out a cloudy jar filled with sleazy, slimy, oozy, wormy, wriggling greenish-black bloodsuckers. I felt sick.

Just about then, Max was seized with a snorting fit. His huge horse body shook, and he sounded as if he were trying to clear his sinuses. I was pretty sure he was laughing.

The doctor proudly set the jar of leeches on the table and then turned his attention back to me. "Now," he wondered, "where shall I apply them? To the left arm? To the right?"

"How about to the horse?" I said, glaring at Max.

Gathergoods broke into hearty chuckles. "Ho, ho, ho. Thou dost tickle me, Sir Robert. And to think that Sir Bevis sayeth that thou hast no sense of humor! But then, Sir Bevis also sayeth that thou hast no honor, guts, or brains."

"He said *what*?"

"No honor, no guts, no brains," repeated the doctor, chortling.

"No kidding," I said, chortling along with him. "So you know good old Sir Bevis, do you?"

"To be sure, Sir Robert. 'Twas on an errand for Sir Bevis that I came to your tent anon. He sent me hither with gold coins to ransom his armor, and he asketh for the speedy return of his sword and his horse."

I sprang to my feet. "What? Speedy return? Then there's no time to lose!" I pressed Sir Bevis's sword into his hand. "Here's the sword. The horse is outside."

"But, but—" sputtered Dr. Gathergoods, "but

what of thy blood-letting? 'Tis necessary to—"

"I'm sure you're right, doctor," I interrupted. "Absolutely right. A quart or two of blood off the top and I'd feel much better. But let's be fair. Sir Bevis is probably worrying himself silly wondering what's taking you so long."

I quickly dropped the jar of leeches back into the doctor's bag and thrust it into his hands. He looked bewildered by the sudden change of plan, but finally, reluctantly, he unhooked a leather pouch from his belt and offered it to me.

"Mayhap thou art right, Sir Robert," he said. "Methinks thou wilt find this a fair price."

I accepted the ransom with one hand and propelled him toward the exit with the other.

"But!" The doctor stopped and stood his ground. "Before I go, I feel I should offer thee some sound advice. If thou valuest thy life, do not tarry here at Hampshire Castle. Sir Bevis hath a foul temper and 'tis not for nothing that he is called the Hampshire Mauler."

Niles leaped to his feet. "Fie on Sir Bevis!" he cried. "Sir Robert feareth no man!"

"Calm thyself, good Niles," said Dr. Gathergoods soothingly. "I meant no harm. Thy nerves are frazzled. Here is a vial of the finest pulverized fingernail clippings to be taken with warm wine." He handed a small bottle to Niles and then turned to me with a slight bow. "Till the morrow, Sir Robert."

With that, he waggled his fingers good-bye, tossed his hair out of his eyes, and bustled out of the tent, his purple robe billowing behind.

6

No more than two seconds passed between the time that Dr. Gathergoods swept out of our tent and the time that a wiry old woman scurried in with tremendous energy, her eyes darting every which way and her ragged shawl lurching off one scrawny shoulder. I recognized her right away as the old woman we had seen earlier hovering over Lady Elizabeth in the stands.

"Is he gone?" she demanded in a loud, raspy whisper.

"Who?" I countered.

"Gabby Gathergoods, that's who. Why, I would not trust that old windbag as far as I could throw him."

That wouldn't be far, judging from his weight and her age, whoever she was. Which was my next question.

I smiled politely. "Now let me see, you'd be Miss . . . Miss . . ."

She cocked her head to one side and grinned up at me. About half her teeth were missing.

"Who be I? Who be I?" she crowed, swatting me playfully on the arm. "I be Agnes Longtooth, Lady

34

Elizabeth's lady-in-waiting, as thou well knowest, thou sly fox."

"Agnes," Niles broke in urgently, "takest thou not a grave risk in coming here without the Earl's permission?"

"Aye, Niles," she said, nodding vigorously, "we all be in great danger. Thou knowest how closely the Earl doth guard his daughter's reputation. Not to mention Sir Bevis. He is a jealous one, he is. Have a care, Sir Robert. Sir Bevis is after thy blood.

"*But*," she continued with a big delighted grin, " 'tis a risk well taken. For 'tis a risk taken for Love. I have a *message*."

She sidled up to me sideways like a crab and squeezed my elbow intimately. "For *thee*, Sir Robert. From *Lady Elizabeth*."

Uh-oh. Trouble. I felt a stab of panic and looked to Niles for help, but he had discovered something extremely fascinating about the tip of his boot and was giving it his full attention.

"M'lady sayeth," crooned Agnes, drawing out each word, "that she doth find thee a right brave knight, most fearless and dashing, and comely to look upon." Agnes snickered noisily into her hand and then leered up at me. "Eh? Eh?" she urged, jabbing me in the ribs with her razor-sharp elbow. "And hast thou not a *message* for m'lady?"

I was as speechless as Agnes was toothless, but she just kept staring at me with her bright, beady eyes, waiting for an answer. I broke out in a cold sweat, and my knees trembled slightly.

Stalling for time, I reached into my tunic, pulled

out a handkerchief, and wiped the sweat from my forehead.

I almost jumped out of my skin when Agnes greeted this simple act with a loud cackle of triumph. "Ah-ha! Enough said, Sir Robert! I will deliver thy message."

Still crowing with glee, she darted out of the tent, ducking and weaving as she went.

Did I miss something? I shot a questioning glance at Max, but he looked as puzzled as I was.

Niles, however, coughed delicately, caught my eye, and gave me an admiring grin.

"Thou shalt never cease to amaze me, Sir Robert," he said. "Not only art thou a master in the arts of war, but thou art a master in the arts of love as well."

"Huh?" I croaked.

" 'Tis no use pretending, sire. I saw the whole thing. Without uttering a word that might compromise the honor of Lady Elizabeth, thou didst draw her scarf from the honored place over thy heart and touch it, as if in sacred vow, to thy forehead."

Astonished, I stared down at the handkerchief in my hand. He was right. It wasn't a handkerchief. It was Lady Elizabeth's white scarf!

7

After that, things moved fast.

First, I ditched Lady Elizabeth's scarf. For good, I hoped.

Second, Niles ate the powdered fingernail clippings. I turned a sickly green and Max turned away, rolling his eyes and flabbering his lips.

Third, Niles helped me out of my chain mail and into a loose-fitting tunic, poured me a goblet of wine, and rushed out to make arrangements for tomorrow's hunt.

And finally, Max and I went exploring.

"Now's our chance," I said, jumping up. "Let's have a look around before the time machine yanks us back home."

Max stuck his head out of the tent. "Sounds like something's going on over by the castle," he whinnied. "Let's go."

We scrambled out of the tent and hurried toward the castle. And when we rounded the last tent, we weren't disappointed. Along the outer bank of the moat, a real, live medieval fair had been set up to celebrate the last day of the Hampshire Tournament.

Dozens of open-air booths lined the moat, and in front of each booth was a large, noisy crowd. There were puppet shows and magic shows and trained monkeys and gypsy fortune-tellers. And all kinds of sports and games and lots of people selling strange-looking foods.

In high spirits, Max and I plunged into the throng. I ate my fill of venison and fresh-baked bread; joined a cheering circle at a sawdust ring and won a wager on a wrestling match; and paid a gold coin to do the polka with a dancing bear.

As the afternoon wore on, we happened onto a group of archers who were competing against each other. With deadly seriousness and without speaking a word, they took turns shooting at a single target that had been placed about a hundred yards away, on the edge of the moat. We watched for several minutes, but even though every arrow hit the target, not one had yet hit the bull's-eye.

It wasn't long before one of the stout bowmen recognized me and stepped forth.

"Greetings, Green Falcon," he said, bowing respectfully. "Wouldst thou care to try thy hand with the longbow? Thou art known to have few equals as an archer."

Max gave me a warning nudge, but I knew I had nothing to worry about. The fact is that I was a bit of a whiz when I took archery in gym class.

"Yea, verily," said I, striding gallantly to the shooting line, with Max at my heels. "Many is the arrow I have shot in the name of Justice and Truth. And now I shall shoot yet another in the name of Sport."

Like wildfire, the word spread that Sir Robert was about to demonstrate his skill at archery, and within moments a large crowd had gathered round. If only Coach Collins could see me now.

I tested the wind with my finger, then nodded for the bow. With something of a swagger, I set my feet firmly, fitted an arrow, and drew back the string. A hush fell over the crowd.

For three seconds . . . five . . . ten . . . I stood motionless, a slight sneer on my face, sighting down the arrow to the exact center of the bull's-eye. No one breathed.

At twenty seconds I released the string.

Straight and true flew the noble shaft.

Well, all right, maybe it was just a little wide of the mark. And, okay, maybe just a little high and far.

The arrow struck high against the castle wall, shattered noisily, and fell in pieces into the moat.

"Rats!" quoth I.

"Yea, verily," muttered Max under his breath.

Fortunately, the crowd thought I was joking, and I wasn't going to tell them any different. I laughed as heartily as everyone else, slapping backs and shaking hands, while Max stood back, shaking his head. It's hard to tell with a horse, but I think he was disgusted.

By now it was getting dark, so Max and I headed back to Sir Robert's tent. Along the way, Max turned to me with a frown on his long horse face.

"Steve," he said, "I'm worried. According to my calculations, we've been here in the Middle Ages for a lot more than three hours, and we should be home by now."

Motor-Mind was at it again. I'd been hoping he

wouldn't notice that little fact. "Relax," I said. "We just lost track of time, that's all."

"Yeah," said Max darkly, "just so long as time didn't lose track of *us*."

If he was going to worry that much about it, I decided, maybe I'd better confess. So I told him how I had changed our Length-of-Stay from three hours to eight hours. Luckily, Max was so relieved to hear that the time machine hadn't broken down that he forgot to be mad at me.

"You're *sure* you changed it to eight hours?" he asked as we arrived at Sir Robert's tent.

"Sure, I'm sure," I said. "And if we just get a little sleep, by the time we wake up we'll be back home in ye old clubhouse, safe and sound."

We ducked inside the tent. Niles was already sacked out, snoring softly. I was pretty tired myself. So, yawning, I flopped down onto my cot, pulled the fluffy cover up to my shoulders, and fell fast asleep.

It's hard work being a hero.

8

I woke up the next morning in our clubhouse back home, rested up and ready to go. The early dawn light filtered in through the yellow canvas, and from somewhere in the distance came the call of a hunting horn. Max whinnied good morning.

Hold it. Hooooollllld it! My razor-sharp reflexes sensed that something was not quite right. I closed my eyes and started over.

But when I opened them again, it was all too clear. We were not back home. We were still in the Middle Ages, Max was still a horse, and I was still a knight— handsome, dashing, heroic, known far and wide as Champion of the Hampshire Tournament, adored by one and all.

Oh, well, I thought, *things could be worse.*

"Ah, thou art awake, Sir Robert," chirped a cheery voice. It was Niles, setting out a light breakfast of bread and honey. "There is time for but a quick snack, sire. The huntsmen are this very minute gathering in the outer bailey. I will go and see that they await thee." He hurried out, calling over his shoulder, "Make haste!"

Max and I were alone. Naturally, I was just a smidgen worried that Max might be mad at me on account of how we were still in the Middle Ages, and he was still wearing a tail and four hooves. After all, I was the one who had talked him into using Flybender's time machine in the first place.

I glanced over at him. But he was just standing there, looking at me with his big horse eyes. He didn't *look* mad. Which was good, because I never like to have someone mad at me if he weighs more than a thousand pounds.

"You'd better hurry," said Max, pawing the ground eagerly. "The hunt's about to begin."

"What's this?" I said, surprised. "Aren't you even worried about how we're stuck here in the Middle Ages?"

"Sure," Max said airily. "But we're here, so we might as well make the best of it. Besides, before you got up, I ambled over to the outer bailey, and I think this hunt might be good for a few laughs."

Was this my old friend Max, three-time winner of the Worry-Wart Award? I should have known right then that he was up to something.

But before I had time to get suspicious, there came again the distant, haunting call of the hunting horn, and now we could hear the restless baying of hounds. The Hunt! My spine tingled with excitement.

"TALLYHO!" Max cried, and he trotted out of the tent.

In a flash, I leaped to my feet, grabbed a green cloak, and followed on his heels.

I had no idea where we were going. That is, I had

no idea where the outer bailey was. It turned out that the castle had two rings of walls, one within the other. The large courtyard just inside the outer walls was called the outer bailey. The smaller paved courtyard, inside the inner walls, was the inner bailey.

Across the drawbridge we went—me jogging alongside Max—through the arch of the main gate and into the dusty courtyard. There, in the midst of a bunch of squabbling chickens, waddling ducks, and rooting pigs, the hunting party was gathering. About thirty men and women were there already. The hounds were darting among the nervous horses, barking happily.

Even Lady Elizabeth was there, with a falcon perched on her gloved wrist. Agnes Longtooth stood beside her, steadying her horse.

Although they were at the far end of the courtyard, and I was nonchalantly trying to hide behind Max, old Agnes spotted me. Instantly, she whooped and pointed, hopping from foot to foot, and then cupped her hands around her mouth and yodeled across the courtyard. "Sir Rooooooobert! Oh, Sir Rooooooobert!" She waved wildly. Lady Elizabeth smiled and nodded a shy hello.

I nodded back.

Suddenly, a cold shadow fell over me and at the same moment I heard a threatening, bearish grunt behind me. I spun around with a start.

Glowering down at me was a gorilla of a man—a man with huge hunched shoulders, long muscular arms, and deep-set animal eyes. He wore his wiry black hair in a tight roll around his face, and a blood-red cloak off one shoulder. His thick lips quivered with hatred.

It was the Hampshire Mauler.

"Keep thee away from Lady Elizabeth, knave," he snarled, clenching his meaty hands into fists, "or I will batter thee to bits and throw thee into the moat as fish feed!"

As I was wondering whether I should teach this big bully a lesson in manners, then and there, or whether I should run for my life instead, the Earl of Hampshire strode up and clapped a hand on Sir Bevis's shoulder.

"Hold, Sir Bevis!" he commanded. "What means this uncouth talk? It doth thee no honor to bear a grudge against Sir Robert for winning the tourney. Put aside thy ill feelings and accept Sir Robert as thine own true friend. 'Tis my wish."

Sir Bevis shot me a piercing look. "What grudge is there to bear, m'lord?" he growled. " 'Twas a fair-fought fight, was it not, Sir Robert?"

Was it my imagination, or was there a note of suspicion there?

Sir Bevis leaped effortlessly into the saddle and reined his horse around. I must have imagined it.

At a sign from the Earl, the hunting horn was again sounded—two clear blasts that echoed off the stone walls. A shout went up as everyone mounted. Then, with the Earl and me in the lead, the hunting party spurred their horses, galloped out the main gate, and clattered across the drawbridge.

The Earl turned to me and shouted to be heard over the sound of hoofbeats. "Sir Robert, I know that a falconer as famous as thyself will choose to join the hawking party. I will see thee anon. Good hunting!"

With that, the Earl and half the riders peeled off and galloped away toward the distant hills in search of deer, while Max and I joined the hawkers as they rode toward a thick, sprawling forest.

A hawking party! I thought with soaring spirits. How medieval-ly can you get? I glanced quickly around. About half the riders in our group had falcons—fierce hawks trained to bring down other birds—tied to their heavily gloved wrists. Not even the fact that Sir Bevis had joined our group could dampen my enthusiasm.

As we came to the edge of the forest, the horses were reined to a walk, and the hunting party fanned out. Each rider picked his own path through the dense, leafy undergrowth. I sat back in the saddle and enjoyed the coolness of the shade.

Until, that is, I realized that Max was making a beeline for Lady Elizabeth.

I sat up like a shot and tugged on the reins. Max ignored me. Leaning over, I whispered furiously in his ear, "Just where do you think you're going, horse brain?"

"Oh, I just thought I'd trot over to Lady Elizabeth and give you a chance to be neighborly," he neighed innocently.

Max was up to something, I was pretty sure of that. He probably thought he could get even with me for writing that love letter to Dawn Sharington for him. But he had made a big mistake. He had put me on guard. Instantly, my brain snapped to attention. My keen senses went on full alert. My eyes narrowed watchfully. And yet outwardly, I remained calm and composed.

A knight knows no fear.

As we pulled up alongside Lady Elizabeth, I gave her a polite nod. She looked pleased and nodded back modestly. So far, so good.

Then it happened.

As we passed through a dark, shady patch of forest, Max broke the silence. In an excellent imitation of my own voice, he spoke to Lady Elizabeth.

"My darling Elizabeth. How my heart doth yearn for thee!"

Lady Elizabeth practically swooned out of her saddle. I practically croaked.

"Oh, Sir *Robert*!" she cried breathlessly. "I . . . I . . . I had no *idea*!" She turned her face away, overcome with embarrassment.

I made a strangling noise. I was pretty overcome myself.

"I am thy devoted slave for life, fair lady," added Max. "Do with me what thou wilt."

Lady Elizabeth tittered up and down the scale, shielding her eyes, blushing a bright pink.

I gnashed my teeth. *This horse*, I told myself, *is done for*.

"My life is a torment without thee, my dearest! Wilt thou be mine?"

Yeeeeeeeeech! My face was burning. I hunched my shoulders and tried to slide down in my seat, but that doesn't work very well when you're high in the saddle. It was more than I could stand. I had to get out of there.

I gave Max a loud THWACK! on the rump, but instead of galloping away like I hoped he would, he capered forward a few steps, and then launched into a ridiculous dance routine. He started with a series of high-stepping prances and prissy little kicks with his hind legs and finished up with a stiff-legged pogo-stick number that rattled my teeth.

Lady Elizabeth dissolved into gales of giggles. She thought I was showing off.

Just as I was getting ready to fall off Max's back, pretending to have a heart attack, I heard the sound of a horse crashing through the underbrush. A moment later Sir Bevis joined us.

I never thought I'd be glad to see the Hampshire Mauler, but just then I felt as if the United States Cavalry had arrived, bugles blaring, just in the nick of time.

I was so grateful that I put on my best British accent, grinned at him, and said, "I say, Sir Bevis, old chap, jolly fine day for a hunt, what?"

He sneered a reply that I didn't quite catch. But it sounded suspiciously like, "Button thy lip, varlet!"

This guy had all the charm of a stinkbug.

9

For a while Lady Elizabeth, Sir Bevis, and I rode together in strained silence. Soon the forest thinned, and
we came out on the marshy bank of a wide river. Turning north, we followed the river upstream.

Lady Elizabeth gently removed the hood that had
been tied over her falcon's head to keep him calm during the ride through the forest. It seemed like a good
time to break the tension with a little small talk.

"Nice bird you got there," I commented.

"Aye," gushed Lady Elizabeth proudly. "Is he not
beautiful?" She held him out at arm's length for me to
see.

He was quite a bird, all right. My guess was that in
the grim game of death, this falcon was a winner. He
was arrogant. Alert. With cruel, piercing eyes, and
long, curving claws. The slow twist of his head was cool
and calculating. He had the air of a born killer.

"What's his name?" I asked.

"Fluff-ums," she said.

"Fluff-ums?"

The falcon turned his murderous, unblinking eyes

on me, as if it were *my* fault his name was Fluff-ums. He flexed his gleaming claws—claws a grizzly bear would have been proud of.

"But," continued Lady Elizabeth, "he is very sensitive and will not tolerate another person besides myself." She tickled Fluff-ums under the chin and cooed, "Wilt thou, thou wittle wascal?"

The falcon never took his eyes off me.

Sir Bevis, who had been watching this scene with interest, broke in with an oily smile. "Why dost thou not allow Sir Robert to test thy bird, Lady Elizabeth? 'Tis said that in the sport of falconry, he has no equal."

"Nay, nay," said Lady Elizabeth, flustered. " 'Tis too dangerous. Since he was but a tiny fledgling, Fluff-ums hath known no hand but mine own. 'Twould be nothing for him to bite off a finger or put out the eyes of one who is unfamiliar to him."

Sir Bevis gave a hearty laugh that rang harsh and hollow. "Thou forgetest, m'lady, that 'twas Sir Robert's uncanny skill with falcons that earned him the name Green Falcon." He turned to me. "Thou art not afeared of Fluff-ums, art thou, Sir Robert?"

He watched me closely with his crafty snake eyes, *waiting—hoping*—for a sign of weakness. That two-bit turkey was trying to use a hawk to make me look like a chicken. Well, it wasn't going to work. Little did he know that I once recaptured my little sister's pet parakeet, Petunia, *with my bare hands.*

"Are you kidding?" I said with breezy confidence. "I love this little killer." I held out my hand as an invitation for Fluff-ums to climb aboard.

"Truly thou art a brave knight," said Lady Elizabeth. She smiled up at me as she put her gloved wrist next to my unprotected one.

Slowly and deliberately, Fluff-ums locked first one set of talons and then the other around my arm, smirking evilly. His eyes never left my face for an instant. Now what? I wondered.

When in doubt, try flattery. I smiled lovingly at the falcon, eyeball to eyeball, and said cheerily, "You're a spunky little birdy, aren't you, old fella?"

I guess I said the wrong thing. Maybe I should have said he was a spunky *big* birdy. Fluff-ums uttered an enraged screech and lunged for my nose.

I flung my arm wildly away from my face with all of Sir Robert's strength. Still screeching, the falcon soared away into the sky.

We watched in stunned silence as he climbed higher and higher. Just as I was wondering what sort of horrible medieval torture the Earl would arrange for me when he found out I had lost his daughter's beloved wittle wascal, Fluff-ums folded his wings and plunged into a dive. It was then that we saw the duck rising up from the river. He never knew what hit him. Fluff-ums struck hard and then followed his kill to the earth.

Arrogantly, he perched atop his fallen prey.

All in all, I prefer parakeets.

10

Shortly after Fluff-ums's spectacular flight, we joined the rest of the hawking party along the river bank. Right away, Lady Elizabeth exclaimed to everyone about how I had tamed her precious Fluff-ums and had made him bring down a duck on the very first try. She said Fluff-ums respected me. He loved me. He looked up to me as a father.

I guess Fluff-ums was well known to everyone there, because they all seemed very impressed. It didn't do any good to protest, either. As far as they were concerned, I must be the World's Greatest Falcon Expert.

Naturally, they all wanted some of my expert advice. For the rest of the morning and into the afternoon, as the hunt went on, people kept galloping over to me to ask "just one more question" of the great Green Falcon.

"Good Sir Robert," asked one lady excitedly, "what diet dost thou recommend for the raising of a champion falcon?"

"Boiled beets," I said, taking a wild guess. "But mark my words: *no turnips*."

51

She thanked me eight or nine times and galloped away.

A short, round-faced man wanted to know what he could do about his falcon, which insisted on carrying off its prey instead of waiting for its master.

I didn't have the faintest idea, but I had to say something.

"Sir," I said, "communication is the answer. Have you ever actually sat down with your falcon and talked this thing out?"

The round-faced man looked confused. "Nay," he stammered. "I have not."

"Then do so!" I said heartily. "You'll be glad you did. After all, if you can't talk to your falcon, then who can you talk to?"

I slapped him on the back and gave him a we-falconers-understand-such-things sort of smile. He nodded uncertainly and rode off slowly. I noticed that he wore a puzzled expression on his face for the rest of the day.

Meanwhile, Sir Bevis wore an expression of burning hatred. All day long he hung back from the group, dangerously quiet. Even when we stopped for a picnic, he sat off to one side. Behind those cold, flinty eyes he looked as if he were masterminding a murder. Mine.

Late that afternoon, the hawking party started slowly back toward the castle. It had been a long day and everyone was tired, so we rode along without much talking.

Suddenly, Max trotted out ahead of the group.

"Did you feel something just now?" he asked me in a low, urgent voice. "Sort of a dizzy feeling?"

"No," I said. "Why? What's the matter?"

"Something funny's going on," he said. "That's the third time today I've felt the same dizzy feeling. And you know what's weird about it? It's exactly like the feeling I had back in the clubhouse when the time machine was just starting to work."

"But it can't be the time machine," I said, ducking under a low branch as we turned away from the river and entered the forest. "If it were trying to bring us back, I'd feel dizzy, too."

Max thought for a minute. "I don't think it's trying to bring us back," he said finally. "You know what I think? I think the time machine may be losing its grip on me."

A slight chill went up my spine. "What do you mean, *losing its grip?*"

"Well," said Max, talking slowly like he does when he's reasoning something out, "remember back in the clubhouse when you pulled the ON lever? You were standing right next to the time machine, but I was way across the room and halfway out the door. Maybe I was too far away for the time machine to get a good, firm hold on me."

"Maybe," I said doubtfully. "But what if you're right and it *does* lose its hold on you? What would happen?"

"I'm not sure," said Max, "and I don't particularly want to find out, either. I suppose I could go into limbo or something. Or end up floating around in time. I don't know. But anyway, I guess there's not much we can do about it. I just hope Professor Flybender knew more about time machines than you know about falcons, that's all."

Before I could answer, a branch cracked loudly

somewhere in the forest behind us. Max and I looked around. A huge, hulking form on a black horse loomed out of the dark shadows. It was Sir Bevis. He had separated from the hunting party and seemed to be following us at a distance. Even in the gloom of the forest, I could make out his brutal, bloodthirsty leer. His thick lips were pulled back, and his teeth gleamed in the darkness.

"Keep an eye on Sir Bevis," Max warned. "He's up to something!"

Actually, Sir Bevis was keeping *his* eye on *me*. All during our ride back through the forest and across the broad meadow below the castle, I felt as if I were being tracked by a six-foot-tall rattlesnake.

Then it happened. Just as Max and I reached the drawbridge, I heard hoofbeats approaching and glanced back over my shoulder. There was Sir Bevis, closing in on us fast. His face was black with rage. Suddenly, there was a flash of cold steel.

"Max!" I yelled. "He's got a knife!"

Max thought fast. He hit the brakes, stuck out one leg, and tripped Sir Bevis's horse when he pulled alongside. As Sir Bevis and his horse veered sharply toward the edge of the drawbridge, I took careful aim and gave Sir Bevis a hefty assist with the flat of my foot.

Over the edge they tumbled. Airborne. The sky above, the moat below.

For a moment or two, things didn't look too bad for Sir Bevis. In fact, it looked as if he had a very respectable swan dive going. But at the last minute he chickened out. With a husky little scream, the Hampshire Mauler hit the water doing a cannonball.

His horse did more of a belly-flop, its legs spread out wide and flat.

The hawking party reined to a stop and exploded into loud laughter. Within seconds, people began streaming out of the castle to see what all the excitement was about.

Sir Bevis, sputtering and cursing, grabbed his free-floating saddle as it drifted by, struggled up onto it, and began paddling for shore. On a surfboard he might have looked good, but on a saddle he didn't. Everybody thought he was hilarious. Lady Elizabeth laughed so hard I thought she was going to fall off her horse.

Suddenly, the Earl appeared on top of the castle wall. He took one look down into the moat and almost swallowed his mustache.

"By'r Lady, Sir Bevis!" he roared. "What means this foolery? Get thee out of that moat. Thou lookest a silly ass!" And, shaking his head with disgust, he disappeared back behind the wall.

Still snickering, the crowd slowly broke up and headed into the castle. I slipped off Max's back and joined them on foot. There is something very undignified about riding a horse who has a case of the jiggling giggles.

11

We had no sooner passed through the archway into the inner bailey than something strange happened to Max. There he was, chuckling happily to himself, when he jerked to a stop and was seized with a long, violent shudder. It began way out at the tip of his nostrils and finished up way out at the tip of his tail. But then, just as suddenly, with a toss of his head and a flick of his tail, he seemed to be perfectly normal again.

Seemed normal, sure. That was because I was so busy thinking about Sir Bevis's wide-eyed expression just before he hit the water that I didn't notice that Max was not his usual self.

I draped my arm around his tall shoulder and said, "Congratulations on the fast thinking back there on the drawbridge, partner. What's your code name for this one going to be? The Cannonball Caper?"

Max didn't answer. Surprised, I stepped back, took a good look at him, and saw that his eyes were glazed, as if he were a million miles away. I reached up and rapped on his forehead.

"Anything going on up there?" I asked.

Still no answer. No wisecrack. No nothing. Just a blank, horsy stare. And that's when it hit me. That's when I realized the terrible truth. *Max was gone!*

I was stunned. I gaped at the horse, but he just stood there, slowly swishing his tail back and forth. If Max wasn't here, then where was he? Probably nowhere, that's where. Lost in the middle of nothingness. Floating in time, just as he had predicted. And it was all my fault.

If only I hadn't turned the time machine on while Max was halfway out of the clubhouse!

We were both in el big-o trouble now. Max was drifting around somewhere, and I was stranded here in the Middle Ages—*alone.*

In my own quiet sort of way, I began to panic. But just as I was about to run back out and fling myself into the moat with Sir Bevis, I spotted my squire approaching.

"Sir Robert!" he cried, a big grin on his face. "I have just come from the moat. Odd's fish! Didst thou see Sir Bevis upon his saddle? Didst thou see him paddle? Marry! Methinks I have—"

Niles stopped in midsentence. He swayed gently on his feet for a few seconds, like a tree in a light breeze. Then his eyelids flickered, his knees buckled, and he fainted in a heap on the stone pavement.

First Max and now Niles? What was going on?

"Get the doctor!" I shouted to a passing stable boy. "My squire has fainted!"

The stable boy took off in search of the doctor. He must have found him right away, because within minutes Dr. Gathergoods was running toward me across the courtyard, waving his hands over his head, his purple robes flapping. Pigs and chickens scattered in his wake.

"Courage, good sir!" he shouted as he came. "Clarence Gathergoods cometh!"

Niles was slowly coming to, shaking his head, still dazed. Dr. Gathergoods knelt beside him.

"What happened?" Niles murmured faintly.

"Do not move, poor lad," said the doctor soothingly. "Sir Robert and I will carry thee to thy new quarters."

"What new quarters?" I asked.

"Why, thy room in the base of yon tower, sire. All the other knights have returned whence they came and 'twould be unseemly for thee, a guest of the Earl, to remain camped outside the castle walls in a tent."

"Oh, right," I agreed. "Most unseemly."

Dr. Gathergoods bent over and took hold of Niles's arms. I grabbed his legs. Together we lifted him and slowly, awkwardly, carried him toward one of the round towers along the inner walls. The doctor wasn't holding up his end very well, and Niles sagged heavily between us. His backside bumped along the uneven stones.

"I think I can walk now," he groaned weakly.

"Nonsense," said Dr. Gathergoods generously. "I would not hear of it." He let go of Niles with one hand so that he could open the thick wooden door to our room. Niles's head conked loudly against the doorstep.

"Really, I think I can make it by myself," Niles protested, trying to struggle free.

"Nay, nay. 'Tis best for thee to save thy strength,"

58

advised the doctor, backing through the door. Unfortunately, he misjudged the clearance, and the squire's shoulder slammed hard against the door frame.

Niles opened his mouth to cry out, but just then Gathergoods tripped, stumbled backward across the room, and dropped his half of Niles altogether. Niles's head crashed squarely into the middle of a chess set arranged on a low table. Pawns, bishops, and queens scattered across the floor.

Niles made a whimpering sound. "Can we stop now?" he pleaded.

Dr. Gathergoods knelt by his patient's side. "There now," he said cheerily. "Are we all nice and comfy?" He gestured for me to lower Niles's legs to the ground, which left Niles sort of balanced on his back on the chess table. "Pour me some wine if thou wilt, Sir Robert. Poor Niles needeth refreshment."

I glanced quickly around the small round room, lit by the late afternoon sun as it streamed in through the high, slit windows. All of Sir Robert's things were there, including his flagon of red wine. I filled a cup and passed it to the doctor.

Dr. Gathergoods winked at me and unhooked a small pouch from his belt. Making sure Niles couldn't see what he was doing, he sprinkled about three table-spoons of pink powder from the pouch into the wine. He swished it around and then thrust the cup under Niles's nose.

"Drink this, lad," he coaxed, "and thou wilt be a new man for it."

Niles, thinking it was only wine, took the brew and gulped it down. It must have been pretty strong stuff, because just after the last swallow, he shuddered horribly, crossed his eyes, and burped.

"What *was* that?" he gasped.

"Powdered bat's blood, bits o' mummy, and crushed garlic," said the doctor proudly. " 'Twill give thee strength and long life."

Niles clutched his stomach, and his tongue lolled out of his mouth. I thought he was going to throw up, but he didn't.

"Aye," continued Gathergoods modestly, " 'tis said that my potions are without equal. But truly, they are but a small sample of my talents."

"Not small enough," Niles squeaked feebly.

"My true greatness doth lie in other realms. Why, in my secret laboratory I have ancient Arabian texts, which will allow me to solve the mysteries of magic and alchemy. Soon I shall have great powers and shall transform common metals to gold, foretell the future, fly through the air on magical carpets! Aye, and even Time itself will do my bidding!"

For a few moments he stood there, captured by the wonder of his vision. Then he snapped out of it, looking slightly flustered, as if he had said too much.

"Forsooth," he said, " 'tis late. I must be off." He gave Niles a fatherly whack on his injured shoulder, bowed to me, and rushed out of the room.

Painfully, Niles motioned me to his side. He was still sprawled out on his back across the low table, his legs dangling off, heels on the floor. Raising his head with an effort, he reached out shakily and grasped my shoulder.

"The next time I faint . . ." he said, breathing hard

and wincing from his wounds. "The next time I faint," he began again, "do me a favor, will you? Just put me in a trunk, tie the trunk up with a thousand feet of chain, put it in a cart, cover it with hay, and smuggle me out of the country. And if you should happen to run into Dr. Gathergoods along the way, tell him that I transformed myself into a golden peach pit and was carried off to Miami Beach by the Wicked Witch of the West."

Miami Beach? The Wicked Witch of the West? This didn't sound like Niles. I mean, shouldn't there have been a "methinks" or a "forsooth" in there somewhere? Somehow this sounded more like the good old twentieth-century U.S. of A. than it did like medieval England.

"Max!" I cried. "Is that you?"

"Of course it's me, or what's left of me," he said, trying to get up. "And what I'd like to know is how are we going to get out of the Middle Ages before Dr. Gathergoods finishes me off?"

It was Max, all right. The old worry wart himself. I guess the time machine had lost its grip on him for only a minute. And when it got hold of him again, it must have missed its target and refocused him a few feet away—right into Niles.

"Crazy doctor," Max was grumbling, ". . . *powdered bat's blood . . .*"

I was never so glad to hear anyone grumble in my life.

12

"You know, Max," I said, grinning, "you seem to be moving up in the world. First a horse and now a squire. Who knows, you could get to be a knight someday." I flexed my knightly muscles. "Or who knows," I added, "maybe a duck."

"Gee, thanks," said Max, struggling to his feet. "But actually, a duck would be fine. At least then Dr. Gathergoods wouldn't notice me."

He checked himself over and decided he didn't have any serious injuries. It was weird watching Niles's face and seeing Niles's clothes and everything, and knowing it was really Max inside.

He picked up a mirror and examined his new face. "I don't know," he said. "This business of changing bodies all the time could get pretty upsetting. I mean, I led a more stable life as a horse. Get it? A *stable* life!" He chuckled to himself. "Just a little horse humor there," he added.

I rolled my eyes up to the ceiling, wondering how long I was going to be saddled with horse humor, when suddenly I remembered Max's little stunt while we were on the hunt. Meaning, of course, those sickening "how my heart doth yearn for thee" speeches he made to Lady Elizabeth for me. Just because I never got a chance to clobber him as a horse didn't mean that I couldn't clobber him as a squire.

"Mercy me," I said pleasantly. "I think I plumb forgot to thank you for all those nice, mushy speeches you made for me this morning on the hunt. How can I ever repay you?"

I went for him, but he dodged behind a large leather chair. He grinned at me over the high back.

"What are friends for?" he said, shrugging. "Besides, everything that Dawn Sharington and I mean to each other, I owe to you. I'm just tickled that I was able to return the favor. And may I say that you and Lady Elizabeth make a *lovely* couple!"

I lunged. Max dived. The chair went over with a crash, and so did we.

There was a loud knock at the door.

"Come in," I called, my arms locked around Max's foot.

The door swung open and in strode the Earl of Hampshire. He looked down at us, shocked. Max and I scrambled to our feet, and together we righted the chair.

"Heh, heh," I said, smiling weakly. "My foolish squire did trip upon yon chair, and I did seize his foot to break his fall."

"Yea, verily," said Max. "Wouldst thou like some wine, m'lord?"

Luckily, the Earl seemed too busy with his own thoughts to notice that my explanation was a wee bit stupid. He accepted a goblet of wine and sank down into the leather chair.

"Thank thee, Niles," he said to Max. He took a little sip, decided he liked it, and then put the rest away in a single swallow. "I came to tell thee, Sir Robert, that thy dinner will be brought to thee here, for as thou knowest, the great hall is even now being prepared for my daughter's birthday feast on the morrow. Aye," he said thoughtfully, pulling at his mustache, "my little Elizabeth will be sixteen. Marrying age."

His dark, solemn eyes fell on me as he said this. I gauged the distance between my chair and the door.

"But 'tis not of this that I wish to speak," he added.

Whew!

"I have been watching thee, Sir Robert, and I like thy mettle. Thou art a champion at jousting, archery, and falconry, and 'tis said that no sane man will cross swords with thee willingly. For this reason, I have chosen to share my dream with thee. And a noble and valiant dream it is—a dream worthy of knights gallant!"

His eyes flashed, and suddenly, he sprang to his feet and began pacing around the small room like a caged lion. His fur-lined cloak swirled when he turned, and his deep voice boomed.

"Sir Robert, I mean to join the Crusades!"

He paused to get my reaction. I was impressed.

"Canst thou not picture it, Sir Robert?" continued the Earl, with a faraway look in his eyes. "Thee and me, side by side as we fight to free the Holy Land from the Arab infidels! Thee and me, side by side in the dust and din of battle, thrilling to the sound of sword against sword! And, God willing, thee and me standing triumphant within the walls of holy Jerusalem!"

He paused again. I was stunned. He and me? In a real, live, genuine *war*? No, thanks. Count me out.

Max cleared his throat politely. "Er . . . pardon me, m'lord, but just how is the Crusade going? Have you had any news from the front?"

"Aye, friend Niles. At last report, I did hear that good King Louis of France, his three brave brothers, and his army of fifteen thousand stout-hearted men were deep in Egypt. There they have met with defeat at every turn. And those who have not died in battle are suffering from disease and starvation." He turned to me with enthusiasm. "Well, what sayest thou, Sir Robert? Wilt thou join me in this noble quest?"

I broke out in a sweat. How do you say "No way, José!" to an earl and survive? I racked my brain for something to say. Then, suddenly, I remembered what my great-uncle Dexter always says: "If you can't convince 'em, confuse 'em." I decided to try it.

I pounded my fist on the table, rattling the chessmen and nearly upsetting the flagon of wine.

"M'lord," I said, speaking with great fire and conviction, "thou hast asked me a question fair and true, and I shall answer thee forthrightly and forthwith. Hark ye! Mark ye! The House of Representatives! I speak, m'lord, of first base, second base, third base, and—forsooth—*home plate*! *Zounds!* For a farthing I would leave my heart in San Francisco. Nay, nay, a thousand times, nay. Dracula and his band of ruthless ruffians *shall not bob for apples*! Ho! Therefore, wherefore, I do say it so!"

The Earl's mouth hung slightly open. "Huh?" he croaked.

Max leaped forward and bowed before the Earl.

"Sir Robert sayeth," he said, "that he is deeply honored by thy request. It is, however, a most important decision, and he therefore asketh that you grant to him a measure of time in which to consider the offer more carefully."

I couldn't have said it better myself.

"Certainly," said the Earl, nodding with approval. He opened the door. "I shall look for thy answer within the fortnight, Sir Robert. Until tomorrow's feast, then." He smiled and strode out of the room.

We gazed after him. *The next time I see my great-uncle Dexter*, I thought to myself, *I'll have to ask him what you're supposed to do* after *you've confused 'em.* After all, Max might not be around next time.

Max and I looked at each other—and suddenly we burst out laughing. "*Home plate?*" whooped Max, punching me. We laughed so hard we couldn't talk. Max stepped on a loose chess piece and went down. I collapsed next to him, gasping.

"*Zounds!*" I said weakly.

13

An hour and a half later, Max and I were sitting alone in our cozy room, surrounded by long shadows and flickering candlelight, feet up and planning a break-in.

Our dinner had been brought to us by a friendly, chipmunkish kid about seven years old. He came in balancing two huge silver trays of food and said his name was Thomas of Uppington-on-Marsh. He talked nonstop while he lit the candles and laid out our meal, explaining that he was a page at Hampshire Castle and had been assigned to serve us while we were guests at the castle, but he would sleep on the kitchen floor as usual, so unless we had some other request, he would leave us now and get some rest, because tomorrow was going to be a big day because of Lady Elizabeth's birthday feast and everything.

I was all out of breath by the time he left, and I hadn't even said a word.

Max and I ate in silence, but I knew we were both thinking about the same thing—whether or not Flybender's time machine had broken down, leaving us stranded for good in the Middle Ages. When we finished eating, I leaned back, put my feet up on the chess table, and said, "So, Max, what do you think? We were only supposed to be here for eight hours, and it's been more than a day. What do you figure went wrong with the professor's fully guaranteed time machine?"

Max shook his head thoughtfully. "I don't know," he said slowly, "but I'm pretty sure it hasn't broken down completely. After all, it worked perfectly to begin with, and that proves the professor knew what he was doing. And a while ago I changed bodies, which at least shows that the time machine is doing *something*. That's a good sign."

"A good sign, *maybe*," I said doubtfully. "I mean, what's to keep you from shifting bodies again, only this time to a completely different time or a completely different place? We could be separated forever. You in ancient Egypt and me in medieval England—for the rest of our lives."

"I guess it could happen," said Max, nibbling on his thumbnail. He always does that when he's thinking hard. "But actually we have some pretty big problems right here, where we are. Like Sir Bevis, for instance. You're in real danger, Steve. Sir Bevis isn't going to forget about how you pushed him into the moat and beat him at the tournament. He'll try to get even with you, and I don't think he'll be too fussy about how."

We lapsed into silence.

"Got any ideas?" I said finally.

"Well, there is one possibility," said Max hesitantly. "I've been thinking about something Dr. Gathergoods said, something that caught my attention."

"The part about bat's blood and bits o' mummy?" I asked innocently.

68

Max glared at me. "No," he said, "the part about those ancient Arabian texts he has in his secret laboratory. Remember? He said they'd help him solve all kinds of mysteries, and that *even Time itself would do his bidding.*"

Max paused. "So?" I said.

"So, let's suppose for a minute that Gathergoods really is on to something about time travel, and suppose the secret formula—or whatever it is—is lying around in those Arabian texts, just waiting for two brilliant guys like us to put it all together. We'd be home free!"

"Do you mean what I think you mean?" I said, snorting with disbelief. "Are you, the Man of Science, actually saying that some hocus-pocus recipe from some moldy old book could tell us how to travel through time? Now I've heard everything!"

"Look," Max protested, "I know it's a far-fetched idea, but right now it's our *only* idea. I think we should find a way to sneak into the doctor's secret laboratory, get our hands on those Arabian texts, and at least check them out. Don't forget, sometimes what people call magic is really just misunderstood science."

Motor-Mind had a point. It wasn't much of a plan, but what did we have to lose? At least we'd be *doing* something. Our only other choice was just to sit around and wait for Flybender's machine to wake up and work. And with Sir Bevis after me, I figured it was a good idea to try to get out of the Middle Ages while I was still alive.

"Okay," I said. "I'm game."

Now that we had a plan, we both felt a lot more relaxed. Max started humming to himself.

"I guess this means we have a busy day ahead of us tomorrow," he said cheerfully, "so I guess I'll hit the hay. Get it? Hit the *hay!*" He snickered. "Just a little hor—"

"I know, I know," I broke in, sighing. "Spare me." A little horse humor goes a long way.

14

It's amazing how a little undercover work can brighten your day.

Max and I were up and eager first thing in the morning, plotting ways to get hold of Dr. Gathergoods's ancient Arabian texts. There was a short interruption when Thomas brought us our breakfast and filled us in on how the cooks had been up all night preparing special dishes for Lady Elizabeth's birthday feast, which was going to be the biggest one he'd ever seen, and even though the celebration didn't start until four o'clock, he had to go now and string flowers for garlands and change the reeds on the floor of the great hall because they were dirty and full of old bones, but he would see us later, good-bye.

Getting back to business, Max and I agreed that our main objective was to find Gathergoods's secret laboratory and to figure out how we were going to get in. I volunteered to case the castle, checking out the towers and other likely hideouts. Meanwhile, Max was going to talk to as many people as possible to see if he could pick up any helpful gossip or rumors. We agreed to meet back in our room and would have synchronized our watches if we had had any.

Within minutes, I was slinking across the courtyard and up a spiral staircase, heading for the top of the inner wall. Luckily, all the local people were scurrying around, getting ready for the feast, so nobody paid any attention to me.

A few hours later, I was just about slinked out. I had explored all around the tops of both the inner and outer walls, peering into turrets, over battlements, down into gatehouses, and through narrow slit windows. All I had discovered were a few sleeping guards, a bunch of storerooms, and some great views of the surrounding countryside. No secret laboratory.

I decided to search the buildings that lined the walls of the inner bailey. I skirted the great hall, the kitchen, and the barracks, and sneaked into a large vine-covered building.

Figuring that a secret laboratory would be in a tower or at least somewhere up high, I decided to start at the top. I tiptoed up the stairs to the third floor. Ahead of me was a long, narrow corridor, with three doorways along one wall and several wall torches leaning out from the other. I peeked inside the first door and found I had stumbled onto someone's private living quarters. Judging from the huge canopied bed with velvet curtains, the fancy cushions on the chairs, and the gold dishes on the table, I guessed it was the apartment of someone very important, maybe even the Earl.

I swallowed hard. If I got caught snooping around here, I was going to have a very hard time explaining what I was doing. Somehow I didn't think the Earl would believe I was just out for an afternoon stroll—in his living room.

Retreat seemed like a good idea. So I took a deep breath, battened down my hatches, and took to my heels. The way I look at it, taking to your heels is always better than getting strung up by them.

But just as I reached the stairway, I heard voices coming from below. It was Dr. Gathergoods and the Hampshire Mauler, and they were headed my way!

I ran back down the hall and ducked into the same room. I might have dived under the bed, but as Gathergoods and Bevis stepped into the hall, I thought I heard my name. I left the door slightly open and listened.

"Sayest thou that his arrow did miss the target completely?" asked Sir Bevis as they passed by the door.

"Aye," replied the doctor, "and did strike the castle wall. 'Tis said 'twas a jest, but methinks the fall from his horse hath left Sir Robert a much-changed man."

"And a much-*weakened* man," said Sir Bevis with grim pleasure. "I must act before he regaineth his strength and skill." His voice began to fade down the hall. "This very day at the feast I shall . . ."

I strained to catch the rest, but it was no use. They were out of range. I shivered. I didn't know what Sir Bevis was planning to do at the feast—but I didn't think it was to ask if he could carve the turkey.

I was about to slip out and follow them when suddenly I felt a sharp tap-tap on my shoulder. I spun around. There, grinning up at me with her beady bird-eyes dancing, was old Agnes Longtooth.

"Agnes!" I sputtered. "What are *you* doing here?"
A better question would have been what was *I* doing
here?

"Why, I live here, in the adjoining room," she
said. Then she added with a knowing wink, "But mayhap thou didst not know that this be Lady Elizabeth's
private chamber." She snickered at the silliness of that
thought.

I started to protest, but she held up her hand as a
warning. "Hisst!" she whispered. "We must not be
overheard." She scooted around me and closed the
door.

I was trapped.

"Ah, Sir Robert," she said, whacking me playfully
in the ribs, "truly thou art a lusty, brave youth to risk
coming here. Lady Elizabeth will return within moments, but should the Earl find thee here, he would
tear thee limb from limb."

Funny she should mention that. Being torn limb
from limb just happens to be one of the two or three
things I hate most. I decided to leave.

"In that case, Miss Longtooth," I said with what I
hoped was a charming grin, "perhaps I'd better buzz
off."

I grabbed for the door, but she backed firmly
against it.

"Nay, nay, Sir Robert," she scolded, waggling her
bony finger under my nose, "be not shy. Soon thy lady
love will return and reward thy bravery with a kiss."
She cackled happily, and then, placing her hand on
her scrawny hip, she added thoughtfully, "Or per-
chance the Earl will arrive and throw thee out of yon
window . . ."

I tried a feint to the left, hoping to draw her away from the door. No luck.

". . . as he did poor young Basil Fitzgerald when he did discover him here last year. Fortunately, the stout lad did grab the vine which groweth upon the wall, and began to climb down to the ground. He might have succeeded, too . . ."

This Agnes Longtooth should have been named Agnes Long*tongue*. How could I get her stopped?

". . . but alas, the Earl did seize the vine and shake it mightily. Poor Basil was thrown in an arc . . ."

Decking her with a right hook was definitely out.

". . . and did land among the pigs. He limped to his horse, pulled himself up, and rode away, groaning with great feeling." Agnes shifted her weight with a sort of flounce. "Or mayhap the Earl would kick thee down the stairs, as he did poor Henry Carmichael, who—"

"LOOK OUT FOR THE SPIDER!!!!!!!!" I yelled, pointing over Agnes's head.

With a shriek, she covered her head with her hands and lunged away from the door. I jerked it open and dived through.

Heh, heh, I chuckled to myself as I galloped down the hall to freedom. *The old look-out-for-the-spider trick gets 'em every time.*

15

Max was already back in our room when I burst through the door. He was on his knees, rummaging through one of Sir Robert's oak chests.

"I don't think you're going to find Dr. Gathergoods's laboratory in there," I said helpfully as I flopped into a chair and tried to catch my breath.

Max got up and stretched his legs. "I don't have to," he said, looking pleased with himself. "The fact is I already found out where the laboratory is."

I sat up straight. "Great! How'd you do it?"

"It was easy," he said, shrugging. "I just came right out and asked the blacksmith where Gathergoods's laboratory was, and he just came right out and told me. It's in the dungeon."

"The *dungeon*?" I said. I thought about all those hours I'd just spent sneaking around walls and towers. "Are you sure?"

"Positive," said Max. "The blacksmith says that about a year ago Gathergoods asked the Earl if he could have a tower, but the Earl said he wasn't going to give up a perfectly good tower for a bunch of crazy, crackpot experiments. He told Gathergoods that it was the dungeon—take it or leave it—and the doctor took it."

"But how can he use the dungeon?" I asked. "What about the prisoners?"

"There aren't any. It hasn't been used as a real dungeon for years."

"I still don't get it," I said. "If it's a *secret* laboratory, then how come this blacksmith guy knows where it is?"

"A good question," said Max, sort of snickering. "Are you ready for this? The blacksmith says *everyone* knows where it is, but nobody cares. And meanwhile, old Gathergoods spends half his time worrying about someone discovering his secret. He has a giant lock on the dungeon door, and he makes the blacksmith change it every week."

I frowned. "Do you think we'll be able to pick the lock?"

"We won't have to," said Max. "Because the blacksmith also says there's *another entrance to the dungeon*—an unlocked door hidden behind the unicorn tapestry in the great hall! Just about everyone in the castle knows it's there, but nobody's interested enough in Gathergoods's harebrained experiments to bother using it. *So,*" Max concluded with the satisfaction of a lawyer resting his case, "all we have to do is wait till the coast is clear in the great hall, sneak down into the dungeon, and help ourselves to those Arabian texts."

"And the sooner the better," I added, "because you were right, Max. Sir Bevis *is* planning to get even with me." I filled him in on the conversation I'd overheard between Sir Bevis and Dr. Gathergoods.

Max looked worried. "There's no telling what Sir Bevis is up to," he said, "so I guess we'll just have to wait for him to make his move at the feast. In the meantime, you'd better carry this, just in case."

He reached into Sir Robert's trunk and took out a small dagger. On its gold scabbard was carved the head of a falcon, with two flashing emeralds for its eyes.

I took the dagger and tucked it inside my tunic.

"And keep an eye on Dr. Gathergoods, too," warned Max. "It looks like he just might be in cahoots with the Hampshire Mauler."

16

Max is what is known as a human bookhound. If there's a book anywhere within ten miles, he'll find it. So it's not surprising that by the time Thomas came to tell us the feast was on—come and get it—Max had already discovered a thin little book in Sir Robert's trunk and was slouched in a chair, happily reading away.

Meanwhile, I'd been saving my energy for some heavy-duty eating. As soon as Thomas left the room, I was on my feet, heading for the door.

"Come on," I said. "I'm starved!"

Max jumped up and blocked my way. "I can't let you do it!" he said. He had a look of deep, almost mournful, concern on his face and a suspicious twitch on his lips. "I just can't let you go out there and make a fool of yourself!"

I sighed. "What are you babbling about?"

"Steve," he said solemnly, "it has come to my attention that you are in need of a short, five-minute course in medieval manners before we go to the feast." He began to pace the floor. "After all, this is no school

79

lunchroom we're going to, you know. This is no crummy fast-food joint. This is a *formal banquet in the great hall of a great castle*! You and I, Steve, will be dining with refined ladies and well-bred gentlemen in an atmosphere of elegance and grace."

"So?" I said. "So I'll try not to spill my milk. Happy?"

Max shook his head sadly, as if I were a hopeless case, more to be pitied than blamed.

"If there is any hope for you at all," he said, "it is in this book." He briskly tapped the book he'd been reading, and then held it up so I could read the gold lettering on the cover: *The Booke of Gude Manners.*

"I found this wonderful little book in Sir Robert's trunk," he continued, "and it has all the latest on castle table manners. You don't want to look like a disgusting slob, do you? A vulgar oaf, a slovenly lout, an ill-mannered boor? An uncouth dullard, a rude and vile clod, a—"

"Okay, okay," I broke in. "You've got five minutes. But if I'm still a rude and vile clod after that, tough luck."

Max nodded and opened the little book with a dramatic flourish. He cleared his throat, peered at me over the top of the page, and began to read.

1. Use not the tablecloth as a nosecloth; nor within hearing of thy lord, trumpet thy nose loudly.
2. Butter not thy bread with thy thumb, nor dip too deeply thy hand into the sauce.
3. Neither shalt thou belch with a full mouth,

nor spit upon the floor or upon the walls.

4. The tossing of small bones to the dogs is quite correct and proper, but throw not a bone larger than thy foot.

Max skipped down to the bottom of the page. "And here's a couple of good ones to remember," he said.

9. If a morsel of food be not to thy liking, remove it from thy mouth with thy right hand alone. But wave it not for general inspection, nor make an unpleasant face at it.

10. Should a guest offend thee with a remark, strike him not, nor throw toward him any article of food.

Was he kidding? I grabbed the book and scanned the page. "Wipe not thy teeth upon the tablecloth," I read. He wasn't kidding.

I looked at Max. I could tell he was struggling to keep a straight face.

"Does this mean," I asked, "that I shouldn't turn the table over if I don't like the soup?"

"Not at all," replied Max, trying to sound prim but snickering instead. "Just be sure you fold your napkin first."

17

Max and I stepped out into the courtyard and joined the few stragglers who were hurrying toward the great hall. From inside came a wild confusion of music and laughter. The feast had begun.

We pushed through the huge carved door and stopped short, staring at the scene before us. In the center of the great hall, an enormous cavern of a room, a troupe of acrobats built a human pyramid almost up to the thick oak beams of the high ceiling, and then, on a signal, dissolved it in a tumble of spinning bodies. Minstrels strolled around the hall singing rowdy songs and sentimental ballads. Not far from us, the trained bear I had danced with at the fair was spinning slowly on his hind legs, stopping now and then to swipe at a pair of dogs that sniffed at him curiously.

Through a door in the wall to our left came a steady stream of servants carrying steaming platters of food over their heads. They had to dodge around the entertainers to serve the guests, who were sitting at long tables that lined three sides of the room. Against the fourth wall, in a black iron grate, a fire crackled beneath a deer roasting on a spit. All around the hall, the smoke from wall torches curled up to the ceiling.

Something on the far wall caught my eye, and I nudged Max. It was a huge tapestry. Even though it was faded with age, I could make out the scene—about a dozen hunters on horseback surrounding a forest, and in the middle of the forest, a white unicorn. Behind that tapestry was the secret door to the dungeon!

Max and I exchanged a meaningful glance.

Just then Thomas appeared and offered to show us to our seats, so we threaded our way to the table at the end of the room. I was surprised that Max was going to be sitting with me, since I was a knight and he was only a squire, but I guess the Earl wasn't too particular about rank.

The table was raised above the others on a platform, and sitting in the middle was the guest of honor, Lady Elizabeth. To her right were the Earl, Sir Bevis, and Dr. Gathergoods. To her left were two empty chairs, and at the end of the table, Agnes Longtooth.

Thomas ushered us up onto the platform and indicated that I should sit next to Lady Elizabeth. There was a brief scuffle as I tried to change places with Max but failed. A fine friend *he* was.

Agnes leaned around Max and called down the table to Lady Elizabeth, "I told thee he be shy!"

Lady Elizabeth giggled into her hand.

Max guffawed.

I blushed and got Max in the side with my elbow. Then I helped myself to a huge hunk of meat.

Everyone else dug in, too. And what a meal! The table was loaded with venison and duck and a whole roasted pig, and cheeses and fruits and huge loaves of bread, and cakes and pies and apples baked in honey—

with reinforcements arriving every few minutes.

The food was great, all right, but I'm sorry that I can't say the same for the manners of my fellow guests. In fact, it occurred to me that I should have brought along *The Booke of Gude Manners* and read it aloud to everyone there.

Even our host, the Earl, wasn't exactly a model of dignity and decorum. About halfway through the feast, I glanced over at him and saw that he was wiping his face—which was more or less covered with sauce—on the white tablecloth. When he finished, he cocked his head back and spat neatly across the table, narrowly missing a passing juggler.

Dr. Gathergoods got into the spirit of things by plunging his arm, almost up to his elbow, into a pot of stew. At first I thought he was stirring it. But after a lot of splashing around, he finally pulled out a huge onion, examined it closely with one eye as if it were the Hope Diamond, and then stuffed it into his mouth whole.

Sir Bevis was no Little Miss Goodmanners, either. With great energy, he slurped, smacked, gnawed, belched, and burped. He even gargled. He spilled things, he dropped things, he threw things. I think he would have *kicked* things if he could have gotten his feet up on the table.

I couldn't help wondering whether Lady Elizabeth was upset and embarrassed by everyone's terrible table manners, seeing as how it was her birthday party and she was the guest of honor. I sneaked a peek at her to see how she was handling it.

She caught my eye and smiled at me sweetly. Then she picked up a bone the size of a catcher's mitt and hurled it into the center of the hall. She had a good arm, too. Three dogs fell on the bone, snarling.

This gang, I thought to myself, would be a great help at one of our famous Camp Wongahana food fights.

In fact, I probably would have felt right at home if I hadn't been wondering the whole time what Sir Bevis had meant when he said he would make his move at the feast. Every few minutes I glanced down at him to be sure he was still in his seat and not sneaking up behind me with his evil-looking sword. Once I caught him staring at me while he was gnawing viciously at a bone. His eyes were glittering with hatred, and his greasy lips were curled into a sneer. He wiped his teeth on the tablecloth.

That was upsetting, all right, but it was small potatoes compared to another problem I had: Max and Agnes. From the very beginning of the feast, they had hit it off together just like two old army buddies who hadn't seen each other for forty years. They punched and poked each other; they cackled and guffawed and pounded the table; they laughed so hard they would have fallen out of their chairs if they hadn't had each other to hold on to. And what do you suppose was so hilarious? That's right. Me and Lady Elizabeth, of course.

Bits and pieces of their conversation drifted my way. For instance:

"Aren't they the cutest. . . . . . .?"
And: ". . . adorable love birds . . . made for each other!"
And: "When . . . . wedding?"

Unfortunately, Lady Elizabeth overheard all this, too. Every time I peeked down the table at Sir Bevis, she thought I was making eyes at her. She went into a sort of permanent state of blush.

But the worst came during dessert, when suddenly a piercing cackle split the air.

"HEE, HEE, HEE!"

I peered around Max. Agnes was clutching his arm, with a huge, quivering grin on her face.

"Truly?" she crowed gleefully. "Did he truly say so?"

Max nodded vigorously. "Truly and verily, he *did*, he *did*!"

Agnes reached around behind Max and cuffed me on the back of the head. "Thou romantic devil!" she cried. Leaping spryly to her feet, she dashed by and began to whisper in Lady Elizabeth's ear.

I wondered whether it would be possible to drown myself in the stew.

All in all, it wasn't the most relaxing meal I'd ever had. So naturally I was relieved when the Earl decided to call it a night. He rose and thanked everyone for coming, wishing us all a good night.

Great, I thought. The feast was over, and Sir Bevis hadn't tried a single thing. He hadn't clubbed me with a bone or poisoned my punch. He hadn't even tried to steal my dessert. *Well*, I chuckled to myself as I started to get up, *that's the way it is with big-mouths. A lot of talk but no action. Talk, talk, talk, talk, t—*

"*Hold*!" cried Sir Bevis.

Everyone froze, halfway out of their chairs.

"M'lord," boomed Sir Bevis, addressing the Earl. "A great crime hath been committed!"

"What means this outburst?" demanded the Earl impatiently. " 'Tis my daughter's birthday and not a time for—"

Sir Bevis interrupted, trembling with rage. "I have such news as will not bear waiting, m'lord." His face blackened into a fierce scowl. Slowly, dramatically, he raised his arm and pointed his finger directly at me. Then, in a voice that echoed throughout the great hall, he thundered, "THAT MAN, WHO SHARETH THY TABLE AND ACCEPTETH THY HOSPITALITY, IS NAUGHT BUT A LOWLY THIEF!"

18

A shock wave surged through the great hall. The guests stared at each other in amazement and disbelief. *Sir Robert a thief?*

The Earl pounded the table with his fist. "Hast lost thy senses, Sir Bevis?" he demanded angrily. "Sir Robert is a knight of untainted reputation and is mine own true friend. Explain thyself. And thou best have good reason for this unseemly behavior!"

"I have reason enough and more, m'lord," answered Sir Bevis darkly, "for I do now accuse Sir Robert Marshall of *stealing Forkbeard's ear!*"

Once again, whispers of astonishment swept through the hall.

"Aye," continued Sir Bevis grimly. "As most of thee here know, my great-great-grandfather, Forkbeard, did lose his ear in battle some one hundred and fifty years ago. This ear hath become a treasured family heirloom and hath been kept these many years in the hollow pommel of the family sword. But, by'r Lady! Whilst Sir Robert did hold that sword for ransom on the final day of the tournament, he did discover the hollow compartment and did dishonorably steal my ancestor's ear."

The Hampshire Mauler turned and locked his eyes on mine. "And now, I demand my right to settle this affair in the manner provided by law—*a trial by combat*!"

The guests obviously didn't swallow Sir Bevis's story, and they began to grumble loudly against him. The Earl signaled for silence. He stroked his mustache for a few moments and then spoke.

"Sir Bevis, I will tell thee to thy face that I do not believe this vile accusation. Methinks thou hast brought this charge of theft against Sir Robert for selfish reasons. And yet, for all that, mayhap such a battle would resolve once and finally the rivalry between thee and Sir Robert." He looked down at me gravely. "What sayest thou, Green Falcon?"

"*If he refuseth to fight*," shouted Sir Bevis, "*he is a cringing coward!*"

"Nay, Sir Bevis," said the Earl, with a slight smile. "Sir Robert is not afeared to meet thee. In truth, what doth surprise me is that *thou*, who wert bested already at the tourney, art willing to cross swords with Sir Robert!"

From all around the hall there were murmurs of approval and even some scattered laughter. The Earl turned back to me.

"What sayest thou, Sir Robert?" he said. He sat down to wait for my reply.

I rose slowly to my feet and looked long and hard at Sir Bevis. Gradually, I allowed the corner of my mouth to turn down into a contemptuous sneer. I remembered the dagger Max had given me, so I drew it out of my tunic and began to pick my teeth with it.

Finally, I spoke—evenly, scornfully, with my eyes narrowed dangerously.

"Coward? Me, a coward? *Don't make me laugh!*" I gave a brief, harsh laugh. "I am Sir Robert Marshall, the Green Falcon. I fear no man! I fear no mauler!"

I looked at Sir Bevis as if he were a worm. Then I ran my finger back and forth along the blade of the dagger.

"Sir Bevis," I continued, "thou knowest full well that I have never laid a hand on thy great-great-grand-father's ear. But if thou art determined to fight, then name thy time and place, and we will settle this matter once and for all!"

The Hampshire Mauler smirked triumphantly. "On the morrow then, at one o'clock in the outer bailey, where there is room for a man to wield a sword freely."

"Done!" I agreed.

Then, with the coiled control of a gunfighter walking the dangerous streets of a western town, I pushed back my chair and strode slowly, coolly across the great hall. Max scurried around in front of me and opened the huge door so I wouldn't have to break my stride.

The guests watched my exit in silent awe and admiration.

As soon as Max had pushed the door closed behind us, I staggered weakly over to the wall and crumpled against it for support. *"I'm a goner!"* I squeaked. *"Done for. Finished."*

Max chewed his thumbnail thoughtfully for a minute and then, in a no-nonsense voice, said, "Looks like we'll have to sneak down into Gathergoods's secret lab tonight. But if we don't find any information on time travel there, I think we should saddle up the horses and make a run for it before morning."

Good old practical Max. I mean, this wasn't the most brilliant plan I'd ever heard, but I was in no mood to be picky.

"Right," I said, testing my knees to see if they'd hold my weight.

19

Hours later, Max and I were standing in a pale pool of torchlight in the dark, deserted great hall. Max pushed back the heavy unicorn tapestry and uncovered a thick wooden door with rusty hinges. A distant bell tolled as I grasped the iron latch ring with both hands and pulled, straining against the weight and rust. Slooooooooowly, with a rasping groan that echoed through the hall, the door swung open.

A cold wind, smelling musty and tomblike, struck our faces. The light from our flickering torch pierced the blackness for a few feet only, revealing a narrow stone passageway that sloped sharply downward. The walls and floor were wet and glistening, and from somewhere below came a hollow dripping sound, like a warning. Three hairy, black, egg-sized spiders backed away into the darkness.

"After you," I said.

Max squinted into the tunnel. "Age before beauty," he said, not budging.

"Squire before knight," I countered, wondering if the spiders were lying in ambush up ahead.

"Tall before short," said Max, shoving the torch into my hand.

I sighed. *Somebody* had to go first. So, holding the torch ahead of me with one hand and groping along the cold, wet wall with the other, I started into the tunnel. It led downward for thirty or forty feet, twisted to the left, and then dropped even more steeply. As I rounded a corner, my foot slipped on the wet stones and I fell. My hand came down on something squishy.

When Max leaned down to help me up, a small black shape skittered across his arm. He yelped, and I jumped up, brushing my head against the sticky webs that hung from the low ceiling. Something with a lot of legs galloped down my back.

I didn't try to find out what it was. I batted at it with my hand, and it landed with a THUNK on the wet floor. Grabbing Max's arm, I pulled him on down the tunnel. "Let's get going," I said, shivering.

The tunnel seemed endless. Downward and downward it went, but finally we saw the dim outlines of a door ahead. Quietly, we crept down to it, pressed our ears against the damp wood, and listened. There were no voices. The coast was clear. Together we pushed the door open and stepped into a large low-ceilinged room.

Jackpot! It was Dr. Gathergoods's secret laboratory, all right. Huge vats of slimy green brew were bubbling over fires, filling the room with clouds of eerie green steam. Strings of dried bats and toads hung from the walls. A long, tilting table was piled high with moldy books, and all around the room were shelves cluttered with multicolored bottles and vials. There was even some sort of Egyptian mummy, with loose gray wrappings, propped against a lionskin chair. In the far corner of the lab was a pile of shattered glass and mangled metal—the remains, I guessed, of a recent explosion.

It reminded me of my room back home, and a wave of homesickness passed over me. I half-expected my mother to come bursting in, demanding to know just when I intended to clean up this mess.

But there was no time for fond memories now. There were dozens of lighted candles all around the laboratory, so I figured Dr. Gathergoods had to be somewhere nearby. I posted myself near the main entrance as a lookout, while Max made a beeline for the books. He quickly leafed through one that was lying open on the table, shook his head, and then checked out several others.

"So?" I asked in a loud whisper. "Found anything on time travel yet?"

"Not exactly," said Max, snapping the last book shut. "I regret to say that when we mapped out this wonderful plan, we overlooked one small problem."

He tapped the books with his fingertip. "We overlooked the fact that these ancient Arabian texts are written in *Arabic*!"

It took a few seconds for that bit of news to sink in. When it did, I gaped at Max and blurted, "You mean we *can't even read them*? Of all the stupid—"

But before I could finish, I caught the sound of voices approaching the main entrance.

"Take cover!" I hissed. "Somebody's coming!"

Max ducked under the table and pulled a stuffed

owl and a stack of books in front of him. I wedged myself behind an empty cauldron.

Dr. Gathergoods swept into his secret lab.

"I will not!" he was protesting loudly. Clouds of green vapor swirled around his head. " 'Tis true I did spy on Sir Robert for thee, for thou didst promise me supplies unlimited for my experiments. But thou hast gone too far this time, Sir Bevis!"

Sir Bevis strode into the lab on the doctor's heels. "Thou wilt do as thou art told," he growled angrily, "or . . ."

He ripped a dried toad off the wall and crushed it viciously in one hand. Then he held the crumbled remains under Gathergoods's nose and let the dust fall slowly to the floor.

I had to hand it to him. Sir Bevis knew how to make a point.

Dr. Gathergoods let out a faint squeak. "But," he argued weakly, "thou art taking unfair advantage of Sir Robert, who thou knowest is not himself. And . . . and . . . the *Earl*!"

"Aye," snarled Sir Bevis, "the Earl. Thou didst hear how he did take Sir Robert's part against me at the feast. For that, he will die!"

Dr. Gathergoods moaned, wringing his hands.

"On the morrow," continued Sir Bevis with evil relish, "I will slay that arrogant fool, Sir Robert. And then I will marry Lady Elizabeth, making myself heir to Hampshire fiefdom. And finally, my dear doctor, the high and mighty Earl will be dispatched, suddenly and mysteriously. And thou wilt provide me with a poison to do the deed!"

"No!" gasped the doctor, backing away.

"Or I will boil thee in one of thine own vile brews and use the result as the poison I need!" Sir Bevis laughed nastily at his joke.

Dr. Gathergoods shut his eyes in horror and then, suddenly, he made a dash for the door and disappeared up the passageway. Sir Bevis followed him, his crude laughter echoing through the stone corridor.

After several minutes of tense silence, Max and I rose slowly from our hiding places and exchanged somber looks. Making a run for it was out of the question now. We both understood that. We couldn't just leave the Earl and Lady Elizabeth at the mercy of the Hampshire Mauler.

Sir Bevis had to be stopped, and it was up to me to do it.

I just hoped he'd be willing to give up his trial-by-combat idea and have a spelling bee instead.

20

The next morning Thomas brought us a late breakfast and a castle-news update. Everyone, he said happily, was in high spirits, looking forward to the battle and laying heavy odds in my favor, although there were a few who thought that Sir Bevis had a chance, but that was silly because everyone knew that those with justice and fair play on their side always won these trials by combat, and anyway, he'd see us later. He had to go help build a platform for the Earl and Lady Elizabeth to view the trial from.

Max pushed a sausage around on his plate. "Maybe we should just go to the Earl and tell him about Sir Bevis's plot," he said.

"We have no proof," I pointed out. "It'd just look like I was trying to worm out of the fight."

"I guess you're right," he sighed. He frowned to himself for a while and then added hopefully, "Maybe I could fix you up with a written excuse from home."

"I don't think so," I said, helping myself to some eggs.

Max lapsed into a gloomy silence.

It was nice to know he was concerned about me, but actually I wasn't all that worried myself. I'd been thinking the whole thing over, and I'd decided I wasn't really in any danger. In fact, I was feeling pretty good.

"Cheer up," I said. "You seem to have forgotten a very important fact. Mainly, that I've got all of Sir Robert's amazing talent right at my fingertips."

"How do you figure that?" said Max.

"Simple. Isn't this Sir Robert's body I'm wearing? And isn't he an expert swordsman? Well, let's face it. That makes *me* an expert swordsman. You see that arm?" I held out my arm. "It's probably made more thrusts and parries than you could count. I mean, sword fighting is second nature to this arm."

Max's eyes lit up, and I could almost see his Motor-Mind shifting into high gear.

"You may just have something there, Steve," he said eagerly. "Hmmmmm, yes . . . second nature . . . I can definitely see some possibilities there."

He jumped to his feet and began to pace around the room with his hands folded behind his back. "I could call it the Theory of Patterned-Reflex Response. Through long years of training, the body has been conditioned to respond to specific actions with specific reactions. These responses are now completely automatic and, like breathing, they require no thought."

Max stopped abruptly and looked down at me. "No use wasting time. Let's test the theory right now."

Well, I thought, *why not*? I was sort of interested in seeing how it felt to be the best swordsman in England. I wolfed down the last of my breakfast and then got Sir Robert's sword and buckled it around my waist.

"Okay," said Max. "Let's say that candelabra is Sir Bevis." He pointed to the silver candelabra in the middle of the table. It had five tall candles in it. "For your first test, how about if you whip out your sword and whack those candles in two."

I shook my head. "Too easy."

Max raised his eyebrows. "Oh? And what did you have in mind, Captain Marvel?"

"Something a little more challenging," I said, cracking my knuckles. "For instance, see that apple? Take it and stand over there on the other side of the room. When you give the signal, I'll go for my sword and you toss the apple toward me at the same time. Before it gets here, I'll make two clean slices through all five candles, and then I'll run the apple through in midair."

"A feat worthy of Sir Robert," agreed Max, heading for the far side of the room with the apple.

I positioned myself in front of the candelabra in a sturdy, spread-foot stance, my hands resting on my hips.

"Ready?" he said.

"Are you kidding? The Green Falcon is always ready."

"*Draw*!" he shouted, and at the same moment, he lobbed the apple in my direction.

With lightning speed, I went for my sword.

A lot of things happened at once.

I jerked the sword out of the scabbard.

It flew out of my hand.

Max took cover behind a leather chair.

The apple caught me in the mouth.

And the sword sailed smoothly—gracefully—across the room and stuck with a loud *twannnggg!* into the high back of the leather chair.

Max peered cautiously around the side of the chair. "So much for the Theory of Patterned-Reflex Response," he muttered.

"Well, look at it this way," I said. "If there's a choice of weapons, I can always ask for a harpoon."

21

I don't like to brag, but the fact is I'm not the kind of guy a person should mess with. Push me a little too far, and you've got trouble. Big trouble. And I proved exactly that as I practiced my swordsmanship the rest of the morning. I don't think I'd be tooting my own horn too much if I said that within a few hours' time I had made mincemeat of those five candles.

And I won't even mention the poor apple.

Meanwhile, Max and I had also come up with a clever plot of our own to counter Sir Bevis's evil scheme, and Max had disappeared for a while to lay the groundwork. When he came back, he was grinning happily.

"It's all set," he said. "I talked to Dr. Gathergoods like we planned. I sort of cornered him in the courtyard and told him we knew all about Sir Bevis's rotten plot. I said it was a pretty dirty trick to take advantage of you when he knew perfectly well you had a head injury from falling off your horse and were in no condition to fight. Old Gathergoods was so upset he almost cried. He said he most humbly begged your pardon for his part in the plot, and that he would gladly help us if only he knew how. So . . . I told him how."

"And he said he'd do it?"

"Yep. Just before the trial, he'll slip a pinch of one of his potions into Sir Bevis's wine. So by the time you cross swords with the Hampshire Mauler, he'll be so wobbly and woozy he'll wish that he'd never gotten out of bed this morning. You'll be able to knock him over with a feather."

We chuckled wickedly at the beauty of it all.

"Of course," Max added, "I had to promise you wouldn't hurt Sir Bevis while he's in a weakened state."

"Of course," I agreed. "By the way, what's good old Gathergoods going to spike Sir Bevis's drink with?"

"I didn't have the stomach to ask, but I thought I heard him mumble something about oil of snake and dried crocodile dung."

We were still guffawing when Thomas knocked on the door and announced that it was time for the trial to begin.

We sallied forth in high spirits. I was wearing my chain-mail armor, green tunic, and sword. Max was carrying my helmet and shield. As we passed through the archway and into the outer bailey, a welcoming shout went up from the spectators. There were hundreds of them, all crowded into the courtyard and along the tops of the walls.

Max and I made the rounds, shaking hands and kidding with the crowd. I bowed deeply to Lady Elizabeth and jokingly asked Agnes if she'd seen any spiders lately. Agnes dissolved into cackles, and Lady Elizabeth gave me a gold chain to wear "for good luck." The crowd roared with laughter when I paused beside two squires holding a stretcher and called across the courtyard, "Hey, Sir Bevis, here's your stretcher! I hope it fits!"

Sir Bevis snarled, baring his teeth.

Then, while the Earl made a speech about "the good name of Justice and those who would sully it," Sir Bevis and Dr. Gathergoods shared a quick toast. They said something we couldn't hear, clinked their goblets together, and drank down their wine. Then Gathergoods tossed his hair out of his eyes and winked across the courtyard at us. That was the signal that the deed was done. Sir Bevis had drunk the potion.

Max leaned over, handed me my helmet and shield, and whispered, "Remember to take it easy on Sir Bevis. In a few seconds the poor guy is going to be sick as a dog." He snickered. "Or maybe a crocodile."

I struggled to keep a straight face as the Earl ended his speech with a lordly, "*Let the combat begin!*"

Suddenly, the spectators grew tense and quiet. They drew back from the center of the courtyard, leaving me face to face with the Hampshire Mauler.

The potion was working! No doubt about it, Sir Bevis was *definitely* not well. He was already beginning to sway on his feet, and there was a glassy look in his eyes. Even his evil sneer seemed ragged around the edges.

Heh, heh, I chuckled to myself. This mauler couldn't maul his way out of a paper bag. I just hoped

I'd have time to get in some fancy footwork, a bit of razzle-dazzle swordplay, and maybe a few flying leaps before Sir Bevis fell flat on his face.

To speed things up, I quickly slipped on my helmet and, with a flourish, drew out my sword. It made a satisfying sssssssst sound. I stood ready.

Sir Bevis gripped his sword and drew it out. SSSSSSSSSSSSSSSSSSTTT!!!!

I didn't like the sound of that.

And I didn't much care for the way he began to limber up, making about a dozen lightning-fast slashes through the air with his sword: SWAAP! SWAAP! SWAAP! SWAAP! SWAAP! SWAAP! SWAAP! SWAAP! SWAAP! SWAAP! SWAAP! SWAAP!

I mean, shouldn't he have been just sort of standing there limply, staring at his sword and trying to figure out what it was doing in his hand?

I glanced over at Dr. Gathergoods, and I was not very happy about what I saw.

Dr. Gathergoods was looking wobbly and woozy and green around the gills. He clutched his stomach and reeled to the right. He rolled his eyes and stumbled to the left. He staggered around in a circle and then pitched over backward, falling up, over, and behind a horse trough. Only his feet stuck up over the top. They waggled weakly.

I felt a bit waggly and weak myself as I realized that goofy Gathergoods had gotten his goblets mixed up and had swallowed the potion himself.

Which explained why Sir Bevis was looking so healthy. He *was* healthy. What I had thought was a sway was a swagger. That glassiness had been a glint.

The Hampshire Mauler began circling me slowly,

closing in, crouching slightly. His sword gleamed in the sun.

Things looked very, very poor in the Staying-Alive Department.

I broke into a cold sweat and began backing away. What I needed now was a brand-new, extremely clever plan. Or maybe just an ordinary, everyday miracle. I shot a quick glance at Max, but he wasn't any help. He was just standing there, staring at Dr. Gathergoods's feet with a stunned expression on his face.

Sir Bevis gave a low, fiendish, gloating laugh. He smelled victory and was loving it. "Now, varlet," he jeered, "I will send thee to thy doom!"

I wasn't about to let him know I was scared.

"You and who else, pipsqueak?" I said, still backing away.

I was about to add that his mother wore army boots, but there wasn't time. Because suddenly, I was upside down.

Upside down? What was I doing upside down? Sir Bevis hadn't even swung at me!

I looked around wildly. There *was* no Sir Bevis! And no castle! No Max, no Gathergoods, no Lady Elizabeth, no Agnes, no Earl! Nothing but a whirl of flashing, streaking lights and a wind that blew and blustered and moaned like a hurricane.

I landed with a crash.

On the old, rumpled cot in our clubhouse. In front of me—wheezing, grumbling, rattling, and spewing steam—was Professor Flybender's Fully Guaranteed One-Of-A-Kind Time Machine.

It looked worn out. It gasped. It burped.

I was home.

22

A few seconds later, Max appeared.

Or rather a large, fuzzy, Max-like *shape* appeared—high up near the ceiling of the clubhouse. The time machine seemed to be having trouble tuning him in. It sputtered and coughed and seemed to give up. Then it revved up with a whine and tried again. Meters went wild. The clubhouse shook. A window cracked.

And then, suddenly, the fuzzy shape came into focus.

It was Max all right, stretched out flat against the ceiling, looking down. An expression of wild-eyed alarm spread over his face as he considered his situation. Flybender's machine sighed and turned itself off.

With a loud "aaaaaaaaaAAAAAAAA!!!" Max plummeted to the floor.

I rushed over and helped him to his feet. "You okay?" I asked.

"It's nothing," he muttered, checking himself over for injuries. "What's a little thing like a broken body?" He glared at the time machine with disgust. "But if we ever use that crazy contraption again, I'm going to wear a parachute and a crash helmet."

I laughed. "Well, what'd you expect from a time machine that can't even tell time and got us back three days late. Did you think it'd bring you back all nice and snug and tucked in bed?"

"Maybe not," said Max, limping around in a circle, "but it would have been nice."

He stopped short. "Three days . . . hmmmm, yes . . . that would explain it." Max went over to the time machine, pushed his glasses back up on his nose, and peered at the control panel. "Ah-ha! Just as I suspected. There wasn't any problem with the machine at all! The problem, fumble fingers, was *you*. When you thought you were changing our Length-of-Stay from three hours to eight hours, you turned the wrong knob. See? The numbers control is still on 003. You turned the *units* knob by mistake—so it went from hours to days to years to minutes to hours and ended up on days. That left the control reading '003 *days*,' which is exactly how long we were gone."

I squinted at the control panel and then straightened up and grinned at Max.

"Do you realize what this means?" I said. "It means this thing works just like it's supposed to, and we could use it again any time we want." I gave the time machine a friendly pat. "Good old Professor Flybender. He really knew his stuff."

"Yeah," said Max, polishing his glasses on his shirt tail. "Even that business of my being unstable in the Middle Ages wasn't the time machine's fault. It was just that I had one foot out the door when you started the machine, and it was never able to focus on me properly. That's why I changed bodies and all. And that's why I stayed in the Middle Ages longer than you did, too. If it hadn't been for—"

"Hey, wait a minute," I interrupted. "What do you mean you stayed in the Middle Ages longer than I did? Didn't we leave at the same time?"

"No," said Max matter-of-factly. "I was there about fifteen minutes longer than you. I guess the time machine just had to work harder to get hold of me. Of course, we arrived back here at the same time because that's the way the machine works. Remember? No matter how long you're gone, you arrive back exactly when you left."

I stared at him. "Do you mean to tell me you know what happened after I left Hampshire Castle? How the battle came out and everything, and *you haven't told me yet!*"

"Sure," said Max. "I saw the whole thing."

"Well?" I demanded. *"What happened?"*

Max shrugged his shoulders and tried to look bored. "It was nothing. Just a lot of swordfighting, a lot of kissing, a lot of fainting, and a lot of splashing around in the horse trough. You wouldn't be interested."

He tied his shoelaces.

"MAX!" I threatened.

"Okay, okay," he said, grinning. "But listen closely, because I'm a very busy guy, and I don't want to have to repeat myself."

"Will you get on with it?" I said.

Max tapped his chin thoughtfully. "Well, let's see.

108

Right after you left the Middle Ages, Sir—"

"Hold it," I said. "How'd you know when I left?"

"Because I saw your body quivering, and I recognized the symptoms. That's how. Anyway, right after you left, Sir Robert took over his own body again and for a minute I thought he was going to keel right over. He looked all dizzy and confused and he didn't even seem to notice Sir Bevis closing in on him. It looked like it was all over for Sir Robert. But at the last minute, he sort of shook himself hard, raised his sword, and charged Sir Bevis. And then, wow! What a swordfight! It was great!"

Max began to battle his way around the time machine, slashing the air with an imaginary sword.

"Did Sir Robert make any flying leaps?" I asked hopefully.

"No, but he was terrific. He made Sir Bevis look like a two-year-old. He just backed him up step by step until suddenly he knocked the sword right out of Sir Bevis's hand. Boy, was Sir Bevis scared. There he was, with his back to the wall and Sir Robert's sword at his throat. There wasn't a sound in the whole courtyard. Everyone was waiting for Sir Robert to run him through."

Max paused, remembering the scene.

"Well?" I said. "Did he?"

"Are you kidding?" scoffed Max. "Not the Green Falcon. He's too noble for that. He lowered his sword and said, 'This fight is not of my making,' and then he let the Earl decide what to do with Sir Bevis.

"So the Earl told Sir Bevis never to darken his drawbridge again and banished him from the fiefdom.

And that was it for Sir Bevis. He just sort of slunk away, muttering to himself and glaring at anyone who got in his way. He tried to kick a chicken, but it pecked him."

Max and I snickered.

"After that," Max went on, "Lady Elizabeth more or less threw herself into Sir Robert's arms, and he didn't throw her out again. In fact, he kissed her. More than once."

I was amazed. "And the Earl didn't tear him limb from limb?"

"No, the Earl looked pretty pleased about the whole thing. *Everybody* looked pleased. Especially old Agnes Longtooth. She was so overcome with joy that she fainted dead away and fell right into Dr. Gathergoods's arms. And he—"

"Dr. Gathergoods?" I broke in. "The last time I saw him, he was lying behind the horse trough with both feet in the air."

"Yeah, but he'd managed to drag himself to his feet and was sort of staggering out to the center of the bailey when Agnes collapsed on him. I don't think he even recognized her. He just lifted her up in his arms and stared down at her, kind of puzzled. I think he was trying to figure out why her tongue was hanging out. Anyway, all of a sudden, his eyes shot wide open and he yelled, ' 'Tis a damsel in distress!' He held her up for everyone to see and then he said, 'Never fear, fair lady. Thou art in the capable hands of Dr. Clarence Gathergoods!' "

"Poor Agnes," I said, chuckling.

"Poor Agnes is right," said Max, "because then Gathergoods lost his balance and started stumbling

110

backward. He tripped over his robe, spun around, and dropped Agnes right into the horse trough. And the last thing I saw in the Middle Ages was Agnes splashing angrily around in the water and good old Gathergoods waving his arms and yelling, 'Fetch my bag! There is a lady in the horse trough!' "

Max and I cracked up and laughed for a couple of minutes straight. Then I asked him to tell me about the battle all over again. While he was talking, I got to thinking about all the fun I'd had being Sir Robert—winning the tournament and going on the hunt and dancing with the bear and booting Sir Bevis into the moat and everything. I felt a little sad. When Max finished, I gave a long sigh.

"You know, Max," I said, "it was kind of nice being a legend in my own time."

I thought about it some more. Then I sighed again.

"And you know what?" I went on. "I really do think that Sir Robert and I had a lot in common. You know, strength of character, quick wit, fearlessness in the face of danger. Things like that."

I cracked my knuckles.

Max gave something close to a horse snort. "Oh, sure," he said, "and let's not forget your famous ability to woo the ladies." He snickered noisily. "I mean, you should have *seen* yourself at the feast, sitting next to Lady Elizabeth. Wow! You looked so embarrassed that Agnes and I thought you were going to try to slide down under the table and crawl away!"

Max almost choked, he thought that was so funny. I glared at him.

"Was your face *red*!" he gasped. "If I hadn't

111

known it was you, I'd have thought there was a big beet sitting in your chair!" He gave a gleeful hoot. *"A big red beet wearing a tunic!"*

Max dissolved into gales of laughter, sort of staggering around the clubhouse for a while and then collapsing against the time machine and sliding down onto the floor. He cackled and snorted and pounded the floor with his hands.

I pretended to ignore him. With great dignity, I cleared a place for myself at the table, sat down, picked up a pencil and a clean sheet of paper, and began composing a letter.

After several disgusting minutes, Max's laughter died down to the hiccup-and-sigh stage. He rolled over and looked up at me.

"What're you doing?" he asked with an exhausted chuckle. "Counting the precious hours you and Lady Elizabeth spent together?" He managed a weak snickering fit of five or six snickers. I waited for him to recover.

Then I looked him straight in the eye with an expression of true-blue sincerity and noble self-sacrifice. "No, Max. What I'm doing is saving you a lot of time, trouble, and hard work. It's the least I can do, considering everything you did for me while we were in the Middle Ages."

Max struggled to his feet, suddenly suspicious. "What do you mean?" he asked. He edged closer to the table and tried to peek at my paper. I held it away.

"I mean, Max, old buddy, that I've just done you a big favor. I've just written your second letter to Dawn Sharington for you. And I think I can say that this letter will live in her memory forever. And it'll be a big hit at the slumber party she's giving for all her friends next weekend."

Max started to protest, but I held up my hand. "Wait!" I said, smiling modestly. "Don't thank me yet. You should hear the letter first. How's this for an eye-catching opening?

MY DARLING DAWN!
    HOW MY HEART DOTH YEARN FOR THEE!"

Max's mouth dropped open.
"It gets better," I said enthusiastically. "Listen to this:

I AM THY DEVOTED SLAVE FOR LIFE, MY
LOVE. DO WITH ME WHAT THOU WILT."

Max choked and his eyes bugged out. He looked as if he had just swallowed a slimy green toad.
"And get this. She'll *love* this part:

MY LIFE IS A TORMENT WITHOUT THEE, DAWN,
DEAREST! WILT THOU BE MINE?

"And I'm signing it,

YOUR EVER-LOVING MAX."

I grinned evilly. "Well, what do you think, lover boy?"
Max gnashed his teeth, let out a roar, and lunged

for me. I dodged around the time machine and high-tailed it out of the clubhouse—with the letter in my hand and Max hot on my heels.

It was a great feeling to be home again and back in the old routine.